mw
PAE 19

Strain Gauges
Kinds and Uses

Strain Gauges
Kinds and Uses

Hermann K. P. Neubert,
DR.ING., DIPL.ING., C.ENG., F.R.Ae.S.
Royal Aircraft Establishment, Farnborough

Macmillan
London · Melbourne · Toronto
St. Martin's Press
New York

© Hermann K. P. Neubert 1967

Published by
MACMILLAN & CO LTD
Little Essex Street London WC2
and also at Bombay Calcutta and Madras
Macmillan South Africa (Publishers) Pty Ltd Johannesburg
The Macmillan Company of Australia Pty Ltd Melbourne
The Macmillan Company of Canada Ltd Toronto
St Martin's Press Inc New York

9" × 6", 176 pages
83 line illustrations

Library of Congress Catalog Card Number 68–19659

Printed in Great Britain by Richard Clay (The Chaucer Press) Ltd
Bungay, Suffolk

Preface

This book is intended as an introduction, for use at Technical Colleges and in industry, to the physical background and practical application of all kinds of strain gauges, including semiconductor types.

To the young engineer or research worker who wishes to specialise in this field it should provide a solid foundation on which he can build his expertise, while the non-specialist may read it as a comprehensive survey without becoming involved in too much detail.

The book is divided into five parts of roughly equal lengths. Chapter 1 deals, in a summary form, with all relevant methods of strain measurement, including auxiliary techniques, such as brittle lacquer and photoelastic methods. In Chapter 2 conventional wire and foil gauges are treated with respect to their characteristics and applications, together with the associated circuitry, and Chapter 3 deals in a similar fashion with semiconductor strain gauge types and uses, the last section being devoted to a comparison between wire and semiconductor gauge characteristics. Chapter 4 is a concise treatment of stresses and strains in engineering structures and materials, concluding with the evaluation of two-dimensional strain patterns from strain gauge rosette measurements. Finally, Chapter 5 provides a brief survey of typical strain gauge transducers, bonded and unbonded, for the measurement of force, pressure and acceleration.

The SI system of units is used throughout; at the end of the book there is a brief introduction to its structure, and a comprehensive

v

set of conversion tables to and from English and Continental units.

The author is grateful for the support he has obtained from many quarters; in particular he wishes to thank Mr. R. W. Pye, C.B.E., for his interest and encouragement, and Mr. W. R. Macdonald for helpful comments and for reading the proofs. In accordance with the nature of the book the material has been drawn from a large number of sources which cannot all be mentioned, though permission by the Controller of H.M. Stationery Office to reproduce some Crown Copyright illustrations, and the help obtained from several strain gauge and transducer manufacturers are acknowledged specifically.

Farnborough, January 1967   H. K. P. NEUBERT

Contents

*

Symbols

SYMBOL	MEANING	UNITS
a	(cross-sectional) area	m^2
a	acceleration	m/s^2
a	coefficient of thermal expansion	per °C
A	abscissa of centre of strain circle	m/m
b	distance	m
B	radius of strain circle	m/m
c	distance	m
C	abscissa of centre of stress circle	N/m^2
C	capacity	F
C	constants, various	—
d, D	diameter, distance, displacement	m
D	radius of stress circle	N/m^2
e	base of natural logarithms ($= 2 \cdot 718 \ldots$)	—
e	strain	m/m
e_1, e_2	principal strains	m/m
E	modulus of elasticity (Young's modulus)	N/m^2
E_e	electric field strength	V/m
f	frequency	Hz, c/s
F	force	N
g	acceleration of gravity	m/s^2
G	modulus of rigidity	N/m^2
h	gauge thickness	m
h	piezoelectric strain coefficient	V/m
I	current	A
j	current density	A/m^2
J	area moment of inertia	m^4
k	gauge factor	—
K	bulk modulus	N/m^2
$l,$	length, distance, gap width	m
L	inductance	H
m	predominant term of piezoresistive gauge factor	—
m	temperature coefficient of gauge factor	per °C
M	mass	kg
M	moment, couple, torque	N m
n	engine speed	s^{-1}

xi

SYMBOL	MEANING	UNITS
n	number, order, factor	—
n	temperature coefficient of Young's modulus	per °C
p	pressure	N/m²
r	order	—
r	radius	m
R	resistance	Ω
s	slope of gauge factor/temperature curve	per °C
t	thickness	m
T	absolute temperature	°K
T	periodicity	s
V	voltage	V
V_i	input voltage	V
V_0	output voltage	V
w	width	m
W	wattage, power	W
x, y, z	orthogonal coordinates	m
α	temperature coefficient of resistivity	per °C
α, β	constants	—
α, β, γ	angles	degree
γ	shear strain	m/m
Δ	increment or decrement of . . .	—
θ	temperature	°C
λ	wavelength	m
ν	Poisson's ratio	—
π	3·14 . . .	—
$\pi_{11}, \pi_{12}, \pi_{44}$	piezoresistive coefficients	m²/N
ρ	density	kg/m³
ρ	resistivity	Ω m
ρ_0	room temperature resistivity	Ω m
σ	tensile or compressive stress	N/m²
σ_1, σ_2	principal stresses	N/m²
τ	shear stress	N/m²
ϕ	angle	degree
$\omega = 2\pi f$	angular frequency	s⁻¹

1 Methods of Strain Measurement

1.1 The Problem

In mechanical as much as in civil engineering a fundamental concern
is the soundness of loaded structures. In cases of simple geometry
and basic modes of loading the load per unit area (*stress*) can be
computed and—when compared with known values of safe stress for
specific materials and particular types of loading—should give
adequate information on safety. However, the situation is usually
more complex and thus requires the measurement of distortions
which, for our present purpose, can be assumed to be proportional
to the inducing stresses (*Hooke's law*).

Consider a convenient (base) length l (m) on a long wire of
diameter d (m) (cross-sectional area $a = \pi d^2/4$), which is stretched by
a force F (N). Then, from Fig. 1.1,

Stress: $\qquad\qquad\qquad \sigma = F/a \quad (\text{N/m}^2)^*$ $\qquad\qquad\qquad$ (1.1)

Strain: $\qquad\qquad\qquad e = \Delta l/l = \sigma/E \quad (\text{m/m})$ $\qquad\qquad$ (1.2)

where Δl is the elongation of l, and E represents a 'resistance' of the
material to elongation (*Young's modulus*, N/m²). From experience
we also know that the wire diameter will simultaneously be reduced
from d to $d - \Delta d$, but we shall leave the detailed discussion of this

---

* Newton per square metre. See Appendices A and B for dimensions in SI
units (Système International d'Unités, based on the MKSA system), and for
tables of conversions to other systems of units. Strain (m elongation per m
length) is dimensionless.

and other effects of two- and three-dimensional stress and strain patterns to Chapter 4 on the evaluation of strain measurements.

The main problem we are setting out to solve in the bulk of this book is how to measure by practical methods, and as accurately and efficiently as possible, the spatial and temporal distribution of strain in loaded structures.

1.2   Criteria of Strain Measurement Methods

While Fig. 1.1 represents the simplest though a very important case of pure tensile stress, structures encountered in general engineer-

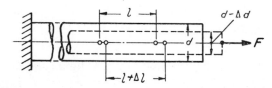

Fig. 1.1 Elongation and contraction of a stressed wire, schematic

ing will often have vastly more complex geometries and loading patterns.

What, then, are the major requirements for *accurate* strain measurements generally?

(*a*) High spatial resolution (small gauge size).
(*b*) High strain sensitivity (high gauge factor).
(*c*) Distinct directional sensitivity (low transverse sensitivity).
(*d*) Negligible reaction of gauge on substructure (small gauge stiffness).
(*e*) Stability of calibration with time and dynamic loading (reliable attachment of gauges).
(*f*) Low effect of environmental temperature, humidity and acceleration.
(*g*) High temporal resolution.

The *efficiency* of strain measurements will depend on the following additional requirements:

(*h*) Ease of attachment.
(*i*) Ease of calibration.

(*k*) Ease of (remote) indication.

(*l*) Ease of evaluation of complex strain patterns from a minimum of strain measurements.

(*m*) Ease of gauge production (availability, uniformity, cost).

We shall not discuss these points here in any detail, but we should keep them clearly in mind as we go along in our survey of strain measuring methods.

Methods of measuring strain are expected to be—among other things—valid, precise, accurate and reliable, if the information obtained from these measurements is to be of a greater value than merely a qualitative indication of stress and strain patterns. What, exactly, do we mean by these attributes?

Error is the deviation from an accepted standard. It may be referred to instantaneous values of measurement, or to other characteristic values, such as full-scale indication.

Accuracy is the 'closeness' to an accepted standard value, or set of values, and is numerically equal to the referred error value.

Scatter is the deviation from a mean value of repeated measurements and is normally referred to this value.

Precision is the 'closeness' with which individual measurements are distributed about their mean value. It is the mean value of scatter of individual measurements.

Reliability indicates the confidence in a measurement which may be affected by uncontrollable random factors.

Validity refers to biases, such as systematic errors of method or of human judgement.

Resolution is the ability of a measuring system, including the observer, to discriminate between nearly equal values.

These, then, are the criteria by which we are to judge the quantitative performance of strain measuring methods. Let us now have a look at known techniques; although we shall be able to discuss only typical examples our brief survey should be fairly comprehensive with respect to basic methods of strain measurement.

1.3 Mechanical Strain Gauges *

These had their origin in the classical tensile test of engineering materials made up into (usually cylindrical) test rods and loaded in a tensile testing machine. The elongation under load over rod lengths of, say 5–20 cm is measured by an extensometer clamped to the test rod. A conveniently readable pointer-on-scale displacement is produced from the minute elongation by mechanical lever magnification.† The earliest type (Kennedy, 1890) is shown in Fig. 1.2a. The

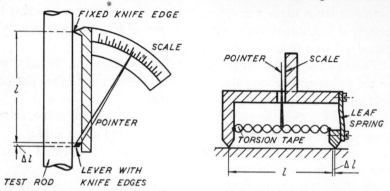

(a) LEVER TYPE
EXTENSOMETER (KENNEDY)

(b) TORSION-TAPE TYPE
EXTENSOMETER (JOHANSSON)

Fig. 1.2 Mechanical strain gauges

elongation rotates a double-edged lever which carries the pointer. The base length must be fairly large since magnification is only 50 times. In order to eliminate bending strain two gauges are usually employed at opposite sides of the test rod.

Much ingenuity was displayed in later years by designing and making mechanical extensometers for shorter base lengths (1–5 cm) and higher magnifications (1000–4000), mainly by using composite lever systems and precision hinges, often machined from the solid (Huggenberger, Granacher and others). Because of their shorter base lengths and higher magnifications these gauges were then no longer

* All so-called 'strain gauges', with the exception of bonded types, are strictly 'extensometers' measuring elongation Δl, not strain $\Delta l/l$. We shall use both nomenclatures, depending on emphasis.

† Clock gauges are obvious alternatives (Berg, Olsen).

restricted to the tensile test set-up; high sensitivity and fair spatial resolution made them useful in tackling problems of two-dimensional (static) strain distributions in various kinds of loaded structures, such as bridges, pressurised vessels and engine components.

A new twist (literally) was introduced in 1940 by Johansson. Fig. 1.2*b* shows the principle of his extensometer. A torsion tape is produced by twisting the centre of a metal tape with respect to its two fixed ends. If this element is then mounted between the fixed and the moving knife edges of an extensometer, elongation will untwist the tape, and a pointer attached to its centre can be used as an indicator of strain. There are several versions of this type of strain gauge with base lengths of 0·1–5 cm and magnifications up to 5000. However, since the torsion tape acts as a spring with a complex and non-uniform stress distribution—in contrast to the (ideally) rigid levers and limp hinges of the types described earlier—the designer of the Johansson gauge is much at the mercy of the tape material.

Extensometers with pointer indication are meant for static strain measurements only. For use with dynamic (fluctuating and oscillating) loads a recording mechanism would be required. The basic principle of the *scratch recorder* was first introduced by de Forest and later elaborated for use on aircraft structures in flight and similar applications (Freise). Magnifying lever systems actuate a diamond stylus which 'writes' a miniature trace on a rotating glass ring. Evaluation is by microscope.

1.4 Optical Strain Gauges

The early optical extensometers (Bauschinger, Lamb, Martens) for standard use in tensile tests had a mirror attached to a roller or a double-edged lever, instead of a pointer; otherwise they conformed with Kennedy's arrangement. From Fig. 1.3*a* the magnification is

$$M = \frac{L \tan 2\alpha}{a \sin \alpha}. \tag{1.3}$$

For small values of α (i.e. for large L and small Δl) the relationship is linear:

$$M = 2L/a \qquad (\alpha < \pm 2°). \tag{1.3a}$$

The mirror rotation is observed by a telescope usually at a distance of 1 m (Gauss–Poggendorff).

Later versions of the same basic arrangement achieved magnifications up to 16,000 by means of extra leverage (Preuss, Geiger) or by replacing the telescope reading by a light beam pointer (Hesse, Berg).

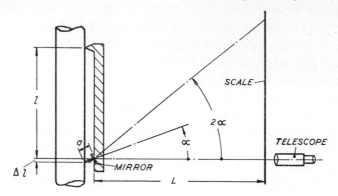

(a) *MIRROR TYPE EXTENSOMETER (MARTENS)*

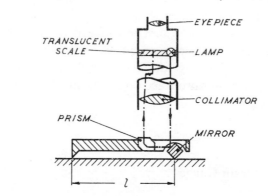

(b) *AUTO-COLLIMATOR TYPE EXTENSOMETER (TUCKERMAN)*

Fig. 1.3 Optical strain gauges

A somewhat different principle—*auto-collimation*—is shown in Fig. 1.3*b*. Tuckerman (1923) employs mirror and prism with triple reflections, while Freise uses mirror and lever magnification for base lengths down to 0·1 cm. The latter type has a total magnification of 12,500 and is particularly useful where high spatial resolution is required.

Some of the optical extensometers are constructed so that they may also be used for dynamic strain measurements in connection with a photographic recorder (Tuckerman, Berg). In the Fereday–Palmer strain recorder the mirror-type strain gauge and the optical recorder are united in one housing. Because of its base length of 50 cm this instrument can be used only on large structures, such as bridges and ships.

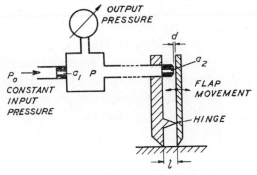

(a) SINGLE PRESSURE OUTPUT (DE LEIRIS)

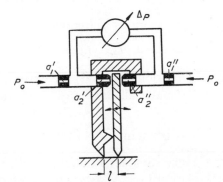

(b) DIFFERENTIAL PRESSURE OUTPUT
(EICHELBERG)

Fig. 1.4 Pneumatic strain gauges

1.5 Pneumatic Strain Gauges

The pneumatic strain gauge principle makes use of the increase of pressure caused by restrictions in a flowing gas stream. Fig. 1.4a shows the basic arrangement (de Leiris/Solex, 1936). Constant pressure p_0 forces a flow of air through two orifices of cross-sectional areas a_1 and a_2, the latter being an 'effective' cross-section which depends on gap width d. Then, the pressure built up in the chamber is approximately

$$p = \frac{p_0}{1 + (a_2/a_1)^2}. \tag{1.4}$$

The calibration $(p = f(d))$ for the extensometer of Fig. 1.4a is strongly non-linear. Better linearity can be obtained in the push–pull arrangement of Fig. 1.4b, with magnifications up to 100,000 and base lengths as small as 1 mm (Eichelberg, Huggenberger).

The pneumatic method is sensitive, robust and reliable. It is well suited to static and dynamic strain measurements. Remote indication is feasible either by piping (quasi-static) output pressures, or by use of electro-mechanical pressure transducers.

1.6 Acoustic Strain Gauges

A taut wire of length l_s (m) vibrates at frequencies

$$f_n = n\sigma^{\frac{1}{2}}/2l_s\rho^{\frac{1}{2}} \quad \text{(c/s)} \tag{1.5}$$

where n is the order of vibration, σ (N/m²) the tension and ρ (kg/m³) the density of the wire material. For any one order, and with $\sigma = Ee = E\Delta l/l$,

$$\Delta l = \text{constant} \times f^2 \quad \text{(m)}. \tag{1.6}$$

The 'acoustic' strain gauge (Schäfer/Maihak, 1919), shown in Fig. 1.5, is based on this relationship. A steel wire is fixed between the stationary and the moving knife edges of the gauge and is 'plucked' by a current impulse in a small electromagnet. Then, the magnet and coil assembly is used to detect the natural frequency of the vibrating string which, according to equation 1.6, is a measure of elongation. The frequency is conveniently measured by means of Lissajous figures displayed on a cathode-ray tube screen, the second axis being a signal of known frequency from a dummy string.

Base lengths of commercial gauges vary between 2 and 10 cm. Although basically a mechanical strain gauge, the output information (frequency) of this instrument is carried by electrical signals which, incidentally, are not affected by the transmission channel. Environmental effects are thus restricted to the gauge only. On light substructures the appreciable tension forces of the taut wire may not be negligible in comparison with the stresses under investigation.

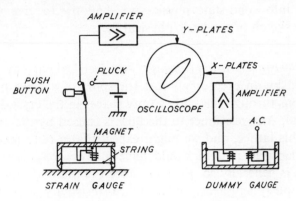

Fig. 1.5 Acoustic strain gauge (Schäfer)

1.7 Electrical Strain Gauges

While the acoustic strain gauge described in the previous section was excited, and vibrations were detected, by electrical currents, electrical strain gauges proper operate by *direct* interaction of electrical energy and its carriers. This applies to the electron current in metal wires (*wire resistance strain gauges*), as well as to the more complex conductivity pattern of electrons and 'holes' in semiconductors (*semiconductor strain gauges*), and it is also apparent in *piezoelectric strain gauges*, where distortions of the crystal lattice generate free surface charges. *Inductance* and *capacitance strain gauges* are effective through variation of their electromagnetic fields. If there are strain gauges operating by variation of, say, microwave cavity dimensions they will clearly come under this heading, but we are reluctant—perhaps wrongly—to let infra-red, optical and other high-frequency electromagnetic gauges enter the electrical fold.

1.7.1 *Resistance Strain Gauges*

This type of electrical strain gauge will attract our main interest in Chapters 2 and 3 on technical details of wire resistance and semiconductor strain gauges, while in the present survey we are concerned only with the more general aspects. Although we shall not be able to go deeply into solid-state physics we shall try to give at least a qualitative sketch of the basic physical facts.

(*A*) *Wire Resistance Strain Gauges.* An electrical current in a metal is produced by an exceedingly fast transport of a large number of free electrons through the fairly empty spaces in the crystal structure of the metal. Any resistance to the flow is caused by the constituent atoms in this lattice, and we might expect that a pure metal with a more regular grid pattern would have a lower resistivity than an alloy. This is generally so. Further, since the thermal motion of the atoms obviously aggravates interference, resistivity should increase with increasing temperature. This is also true, and metals generally are said to have a 'positive' temperature coefficient of resistance. Speculating on possible ways of reducing this effect, we might try to concoct alloys in which the thermal motion is counteracted, or inhibited, by internal stresses of thermal or perhaps magnetic origin. Such alloys do exist, containing almost invariably ferromagnetic nickel, which is probably effective through its magneto-strictive properties. However, one might suspect that this happy state of affairs can apply only over limited temperature ranges, and this, unfortunately, is also true.

From the foregoing we can now readily accept that strain induced in a wire will increase the resistance, since the crystal lattice is bound to distort as the wire becomes longer and thinner (accounting for Δl and $-\Delta d$), but it is likely that the characteristic three-dimensional atomic pattern of a particular metal will also be affected, and thus its resistivity. We shall cater for this variation by introducing $\partial \rho$ as a contribution to the (measurable) resistance variation dR, and obtain for an applied stress variation $d\sigma$, at constant temperature:

$$\frac{\mathrm{d}R}{\mathrm{d}\sigma} = \frac{\mathrm{d}(\rho l/a)}{\mathrm{d}\sigma} = \frac{\rho}{a} \cdot \frac{\partial l}{\partial \sigma} - \frac{\rho}{a^2} \cdot \frac{\partial a}{\partial \sigma} + \frac{l}{a} \cdot \frac{\partial \rho}{\partial \sigma} \qquad (1.7)$$

or, dividing by the initial resistance $R = \rho l/a$ and replacing the differentials by small but finite increments,*

$$\frac{\Delta R}{R} = \frac{\Delta l}{l} - \frac{\Delta a}{a} + \frac{\Delta \rho}{\rho}. \tag{1.8}$$

With $\Delta a/a = 2\Delta d/d$, and introducing *Poisson's ratio* ν (see Chapter 4), the lateral contraction of the wire becomes

$$\frac{\Delta d}{d} = -\nu\frac{\Delta l}{l} \tag{1.9}$$

or, from equations 1.8 and 1.9,

$$\frac{\Delta R}{R} = \frac{\Delta l}{l}(1 + 2\nu) + \frac{\Delta \rho}{\rho}. \tag{1.10}$$

The *gauge factor* k (strain sensitivity), therefore, is

$$k = \frac{\Delta R/R}{\Delta l/l} = 1 + 2\nu + \frac{\Delta \rho/\rho}{\Delta l/l}. \tag{1.11}$$

Now, for most metals, $\nu = 0\cdot3$, and thus the gauge factor

$$k = 1\cdot6 + \frac{\Delta \rho/\rho}{\Delta l/l}. \tag{1.12}$$

This is an interesting result, since experimental evidence shows that k is almost invariably greater than $1\cdot6$. There *must*, therefore, be some variation of resistivity in these wires. In fact, many useful alloys with small temperature coefficients of resistivity, such as the Constantan group of copper–nickel alloys, have a gauge factor close to 2 which—as can easily be shown—is also that of metal wires stretched beyond their elastic range. Here, then, is a chance to measure high and low values of strain with one gauge of constant gauge factor for the whole range (Fig. 1.6c). Other alloys, and most pure metals, are less obliging, and nickel in particular has a very uneven gauge factor.

In 1856 Lord Kelvin exposed a piece of wire to hydrostatic pressure and so measured the depth of water. Carlson had used a metal wire gauge as early as 1930, but it was the pioneering work of E. E. Simmons at the Californian Institute of Technology and, independently, of A. C. Ruge at the Massachusetts Institute of

* This is permissible if $\partial l/\partial \sigma$, $\partial \alpha/\partial \sigma$ and $\partial \rho/\partial \sigma$ are nearly constants in an essentially linear system.

Technology, which in 1937 really started the modern wire resistance strain gauge on its triumphant path. Ruge actually cemented a fine-wire grid, together with thicker terminal wires, on to a thin piece of paper and this in turn on to the substructure, thus creating the

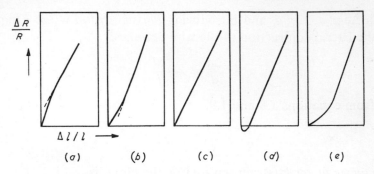

(a)   IRON, HARD DRAWN COPPER, SILVER, PLATINUM,
10% IRIDIUM-PLATINUM, 10% RHODIUM-PLATINUM.

(b)   40% SILVER-PALLADIUM.

(c)   'FERRY', ANNEALED COPPER.

(d)   NICKEL.

(e)   'MINALPHA.'

Fig. 1.6 Strain sensitivity of some metals and alloys
(*Crown Copyright*)

bonded wire resistance strain gauge as we know it today. It is now manufactured and used in large quantities all over the world. There are also some derivations of the original wire gauge, such as the 'printed' foil gauge made from thin metal foil by a photo-mechanical etching process (Jackson, 1953) and the so-called 'self-adhesive' strain gauge which makes use of the adhesion of a thin elastomer strip to a highly polished surface (Hickson, 1959).

Wire resistance strain gauges are usually operated in Wheatstone bridge circuits. In the simplest case of Fig. 1.7 the bridge was initially at balance condition. On the application of strain e (m/m) one resistance (the strain gauge) increases by $\Delta R = ekR$ and the output current in the galvanometer of resistance R_g becomes

$$I = \frac{V_i k e}{2(R + R_1 + 2R_g)} \qquad (\Delta R \ll R) \qquad (1.13)$$

and the output voltage across R_g is

$$V_o = IR_g = \frac{V_ike}{2\{2 + (R + R_1)/R_g\}}.$$ (1.14)

When the galvanometer is replaced by a high-impedance amplifier input, $R_g \to \infty$, and

$$V_o' = \tfrac{1}{4}V_ike.$$ (1.15)

If, as an illustration, $V_i = 10$ V, $k = 2$ and $e = 10^{-3}$, then $V_o' = 5$ mV. A push–pull arrangement with two active gauges would give twice that output, and if all four arms of the bridge were active the output voltage would be four times that of equation 1.15. Notice

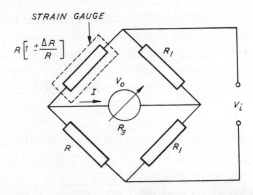

Fig. 1.7 Basic bridge circuit with one active strain gauge

that since the bridge output (current or voltage) is proportional to strain $e = \Delta l/l$—and not to Δl as with extensometers—the bonded resistance strain gauge in a bridge circuit is a genuine strain gauge.

A host of subsidiary electronic and recording equipment essential for the accurate and efficient measurement of static and dynamic strain has during the years grown around the wire resistance strain gauge and is now in wide and constant use.

The smallest base length is about 3 mm, but since the widths of these small gauges become comparable with their lengths, sensitivity to lateral strain is no longer negligible. However, the major limitation of wire resistance strain gauges is their small output. The low value of the gauge factor combined with only moderate values of gauge resistance and permissible current densities (in order to avoid over-heating) puts wire resistance gauges—like thermocouples—firmly into the low-output class of transducers, and the effect of ambient temperature variations on gauge resistance might—if not watched carefully—be of the same order as those caused by strain. This low-level output has also proved an embarrassment in time-multiplexed switching for multiple-gauge recording.

Bonded wire resistance strain gauges are also used as sensing elements in transducers for the measurement of various physical quantities, such as force, pressure, acceleration, etc., as will be shown in Chapter 5.

For the moment the few notes given above may suffice; the construction, properties and uses of wire resistance strain gauges will be treated in detail in Chapter 2, though we can already deduce from the foregoing why desperate efforts have been made to find gauges of similar properties (resistive character, small size, ease of attachment, low cost), but of higher sensitivity. Whether the semiconductor strain gauge today is more than a promise we shall discuss in the section to follow and, in greater technical detail, in Chapter 3 of this book.

(B) Semiconductor Strain Gauges.   Strain sensitivities about an order of magnitude higher than those of wire resistance gauges were indeed observed on strips machined from carbon compound resistors (Kearus, Guerke, 1937) and used on rotating air screws. Strips of colloidal graphite in alcoholic solution painted on to the test specimen had gauge factors approaching 20 (Hull) and even force measuring ring configurations with four of these elements, constituting a complete Wheatstone bridge, have been devised (Theiss). However, these 'semiconductor' gauges of old operated simply on contact resistance variations between the carbon grains—like carbon pile * regulators and carbon grain microphones—and thus suffered excessive hysteresis, zero shift and variation with temperature of resistance. They are now superseded by gauges based on silicon and germanium (C. S. Smith, 1954; Mason and Thurston, 1957).

How can we visualise the conduction process in these new materials? A valence electron in pure silicon or germanium can be excited into the conduction band where it participates in the conduction of electrical current. The vacancy (or *hole*) left behind also

_____

* There was actually a carbon pile strain gauge (Bernhard, 1927).

serves as a current carrier, for in an electric field it travels through the crystal like a positive charge, the vacated position being filled by an electron from an adjacent atom. However, the excitation voltage (about 1 eV) required for this process is fairly high; the resistivity of pure ('intrinsic') semiconductors is therefore also relatively high.

Doped semiconductor materials contain minute quantities of foreign atoms from either the third or the fifth group of the periodic system. Considering first an element of the fifth group, such as phosphorus, there are four perfect bonds with the four valence electrons of silicon or germanium. The fifth valence electron of the phosphorus atom remains only weakly attached, and a relatively small energy (about 0·05 eV) suffices to excite it into the conduction band where it serves as a current carrier, till it is captured by a phosphorus atom which has lost its surplus electron. This process is known as *n*-conduction, by *negative* electrons. The conductivity of *n*-doped silicon (or germanium) is higher than that of the pure semiconductor, because of the much smaller energy required to initiate the process.

Similarly, an atom of the third group, such as boron, produces three perfect bonds with the silicon atom; the fourth again is weak and an energy of only 0·08 eV is required to fill the hole by an electron from an adjacent silicon atom. This mechanism is known as *p*-conduction, by *positive* vacancies, or holes.

Resistivity, and variation of resistivity with temperature, of doped semiconductors generally decrease with increasing amounts of doping. Also, since the numbers of foreign atoms in doped material is limited, at higher temperatures the resistance/temperature characteristic of a doped semiconductor approaches that of the pure material which varies *inversely* with temperature according to

$$\rho = \alpha e^{\beta/T}$$

where T (°K) is the absolute temperature, α and β are constants and e ($= 2·718$) is the base of the natural logarithms.

The piezoresistive effect, i.e. the variation of resistance with strain in strips of silicon or germanium, pure or doped, can in essence be reduced to anisotropic variations of the carrier mobilities in these materials, which would also explain the fact that the piezoresistive sensitivity is substantially independent of the resistivity level of a particular semiconductor material.

The gauge factor k of semiconductor gauges can be written in a similar form to equation 1.11,

$$k = \frac{\Delta R/R}{\Delta l/l} = 1 + 2\nu + m \qquad (1.16)$$

where for silicon and germanium the lateral contraction term with Poisson's ratio ν lies between 0·3 and 0·6 and so can be neglected in comparison with the last term, the product of the piezoresistive co-efficient π (m²/N) and Young's modulus E (N/m²). π and E depend on material, crystal orientation and relative position of the direction of current and stress (e.g. tension, shear or hydraulic compression), but as a rough guide it may assume the maximum values * of Table 1.1.

TABLE 1.1   Maximum Values of m at Room Temperature (Smith)

MATERIAL	p-silicon	n-silicon	p-germanium	n-germanium
m_{max}	+175	−133	+102	−157

Gauge factors of semiconductor silicon and germanium strain gauges are therefore at least 50 times higher than those of wire gauges; they also offer negative values of k which would permit the side-by-side use of, say, p-Si and n-Si gauges connected in adjacent arms of a bridge circuit.

The temperature coefficients of resistance of pure silicon and germanium are high, and prior to the development of doped materials the application of these gauges for accurate measurements seemed rather doubtful. Fortunately, the temperature coefficient of resistivity and of gauge factor proved to depend critically on the kind and degree of doping (Figs. 1.8a and b), so that high gauge factors can be obtained without undue loss of stability at variable ambient temperatures but, more than with wire resistance strain gauges, the user of semiconductor strain gauges is here entirely in the hands of the gauge manufacturers.

The discussion of technical details of the properties, bonding techniques and uses of semiconductor strain gauges must be deferred to Chapter 3, which will also treat of the specific circuit requirements pertaining to the much larger resistance variations of these gauges.

Semiconductor strain gauges have also been used as sensing

* These maximum values are not necessarily related to the same crystal orientation.

elements in transducers for the measurement of force, pressure and acceleration, particularly where only low strain levels—but at civilised environmental conditions—were available. Recently, electrically insulated *p–n*-junctions have been produced by diffusion of suitable impurities into selected surface areas of a monolithic piece of pure semiconductor material. In this fashion beam elements sensitive to bending and pressure-sensitive diaphragms have been made (Pfann and Thurston, 1961).

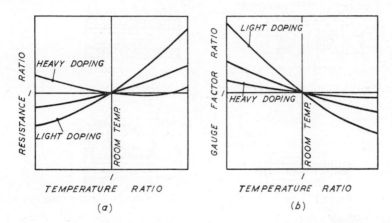

Fig. 1.8 Variation with temperature, schematic, of (*a*) resistance and (*b*) gauge factor of *p*-type silicon at various degrees of doping

1.7.2   *Inductance Strain Gauges*

After the advent of the resistance strain gauge, is there today still room for other types of electrical strain gauges? This question especially arises with regard to inductance strain gauges, of which there has been a prolific crop of types, particularly on the Continent.

The earliest types were contemporaries of the wire resistance strain gauge (Ratzke, 1937; Thum and others, 1938) which have been developed extensively during the nineteen-forties, since they satisfied the great need for electrical remote recording. Later on, when in competition with wire resistance gauges, they still gave a higher output and often better stability of measurement. Also, they can be calibrated individually, and since they are extensometers, spatial resolution down to 1 mm is possible.

On the other hand they require a more complex a.c. circuitry, are often more delicate and always more expensive.

Fig. 1.9 shows schematically various ways of transforming a linear displacement Δl into an inductance variation ΔL assuming that for reasons of sensitivity and linearity a push–pull arrangement would usually be preferred to single-coil units. The transverse-armature

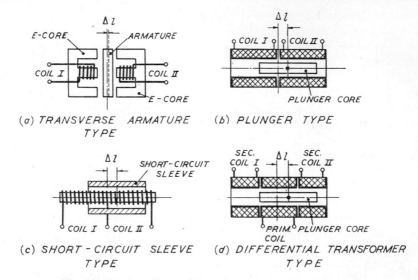

Fig. 1.9 Push–pull variable inductance gauges, schematic

type has the highest sensitivity, which in the plunger and the short-circuit ring type is bartered for a wider linear range. The differential-transformer type is perhaps better known as a pick-off for the measurement of displacement generally; there is, however, at least one strain gauge (Philips) based on this principle.

The accurate expressions for the strain sensitivity of variable-inductance gauges are rather complex (because of extra contributions from resistance variations), though in the linear range of a well-designed inductance gauge with a high reactance/resistance ratio $\Delta L/L$ is proportional to $\Delta l/l'$, where in a transverse-armature type l' is the width of the magnetic air gap, not the base length of the gauge.

The double-coil (push–pull) arrangements of Fig. 1.9 are connected in adjacent arms of an a.c.-fed bridge which is initially at balance (Fig. 1.10). The bridge output, then, is an amplitude-modulated carrier of 2–20 kc/s frequency. The information (static or dynamic strain) is thus enshrined in amplitude and frequency of the modulation and must be extracted, prior to recording, by demodulation (rectification and carrier removal). Carrier amplification and phase-sensitive demodulation are refinements common in this kind of measuring system.

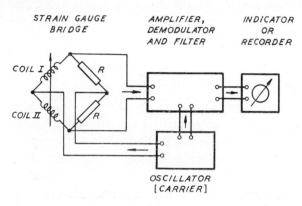

STRAIN GAUGE BRIDGE   AMPLIFIER, DEMODULATOR AND FILTER   INDICATOR OR RECORDER

COIL I   R

COIL II   R

OSCILLATOR [CARRIER]

Fig. 1.10 Carrier system for inductance strain gauges

Base lengths of commercial inductance strain gauges vary between 1 and 5 cm for the general-purpose types (Brosa, Askania, Vibrometer, Hottinger) and between 1 and 5 mm in high-resolution gauges (Askania, Vibrometer). Maximum over-all sensitivity of strain measuring systems with inductance gauges approaches 10^{-5} m/m per cm indicator deflexion. The useful signal frequency band is limited to about one tenth of the carrier frequency.

1.7.3   *Capacitance Strain Gauges*

Although the methods for producing variation of capacitance are numerous and diverse the accurate measurement of small capacitance variations is difficult. Unless one is prepared to use extremely narrow air gaps—which, in turn, might cause large temperature errors—the passive capacitance of connecting cables severely reduces the useful capacitance variation of the gauge. In conventional a.c. bridge circuits stray capacities to earth aggravate the effect and are liable to introduce spurious signals. Also, extremely high carrier frequencies

are required in order to avoid excessive values of circuit impedance. It is therefore not surprising that the only capacitance strain gauge on record (Carter, 1945) has not survived.

However, in more recent years capacitance-type transducers have succeeded in applications other than strain measurement. This has been made possible by a more sophisticated type of high-frequency bridge with tightly coupled ratio arms (Blumlein) and one cannot be sure that capacitance strain gauges may not be resurrected at some future time, particularly for use at high ambient temperatures.

1.7.4 *Piezoelectric Strain Gauges*

A natural piezoelectric crystal (e.g. quartz) or a slab of polarised polycrystalline ceramic (e.g. barium titanate) under stress generates free electic surface charges which, when allowed to leak away through a resistance, produce a voltage across it proportional to the stress. However, the duration of this process is finite and piezoelectric sensors are thus suitable for dynamic measurements only.

Consider a slab of piezoelectric material with an active length-expander mode, cemented to a substructure under stress. Fig. 1.11 shows a commercial gauge (G.E.C. Ltd.) made of barium titanate. The output voltage across the slab terminals is

$$V = het \quad \text{(V)} \qquad (1.17)$$

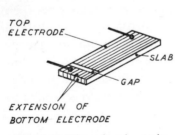

Fig. 1.11 Piezoelectric strain gauge (Koren)

where e (m/m) is the (instantaneous) strain, t (m) the slab thickness and h (V/m) the piezoelectric strain co-efficient. For instance, a quartz slab of 1 mm thickness would thus produce an output of about 4·5 V at a strain of only $e = 10^{-6}$ m/m. A similar slab of barium titanate is about ten times less sensitive, because of its higher dielectric constant, although it has a higher coupling coefficient. Anyway, in actual measurement the available voltage would be considerably less (because of extra circuit capacitance, etc.), though still high enough to make piezoelectric strain gauges attractive for the measurement of small dynamic strains (Koren, 1949). They have, for instance, been employed on vibrating steam turbine blades with an over-all sensitivity of 100 mV per 10^{-6} strain (Luck and Kell, 1956) and on diaphragms of dynamic pressure gauges (Edwards, 1957).

1.7.5 *Photoelectric Strain Gauges*

In the photoelectric strain gauge of Fig. 1.12 the amount of light incident on a photo cell is made a measure of strain by a variable slit in the light passage (Lehr, 1936). The mechanical magnification of the

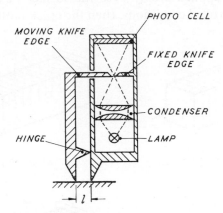

Fig. 1.12 Photoelectric strain gauge (Lehr)

particular instrument was 50 and the over-all magnification, up to reading the photo current on a microammeter scale, 300,000. Standard base lengths were 1 and 2 mm.

Constancy of calibration depended on the stability of the photo cell and, particularly, of the miniature lamp, which proved a perpetual source of anxiety. An obvious improvement by employing two independent light paths (one with a fixed slit) was not attempted, perhaps because of added complication and bulk.

1.8 Miscellaneous Methods

In this section we shall try to give a brief survey of experimental methods which are either complementary to strain gauging proper, such as the brittle lacquer technique, or independent methods suitable

B

for the measurement of two-dimensional strain patterns, such as photoelastic and X-ray techniques. A moiré fringe method (Bromley, 1956) and the replica technique (Hickson, 1959) can only be mentioned here.

1.8.1   *Brittle Lacquer Method*

If a lacquer coat which clings well to a surface, but cracks easily at tensile stress, is applied evenly over the surface of a structure and dried under controlled conditions, then the crack pattern obtained on

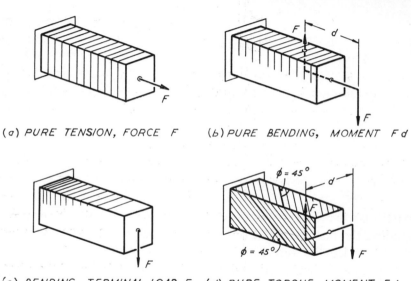

(*a*) PURE TENSION, FORCE F   (*b*) PURE BENDING, MOMENT F *d*

(*c*) BENDING, TERMINAL LOAD F   (*d*) PURE TORQUE, MOMENT F *d*

Fig. 1.13 Typical crack patterns on a beam under basic modes of loading

loading the structure provides useful information on the existing two-dimensional strain pattern which is evaluated after the removal of the load. The relative spacing of the cracks indicates the degree of local strain, with the directions of principal strain normal to the crack lines. Figs. 1.13 *a–d* show typical crack patterns on a beam of rectangular cross section, loaded in different manners by forces or moments.

For a quantitative analysis of brittle lacquer patterns a metal strip is covered with an identical lacquer coat and dried under identical conditions. Then, at a standard load applied according to Fig. 1.13*c* a crack pattern is produced which can be 'calibrated' against a strain scale placed alongside the metal strip. Comparison of line densities in appropriate regions of the test structure and on the calibration strip is said to be possible to within an error of 10–20%.

The mode of loading of a structure under test can be deduced from the angle ϕ between the crack lines and the axes of torque or bending, as the case may be, according to

$$\tan 2\phi = 2\tau/\sigma \qquad (1.18)$$

where σ and τ are the tensile and shear stresses, respectively. For instance, Fig. 1.13*a* has $\tau \to 0$ for $\phi = 90°$, and Fig. 1.13*d* has $\sigma \to 0$ for $\phi = 45°$.

It is clear from the foregoing that the brittle lacquer method is extremely valuable as a preliminary to a detailed strain analysis by individual gauges, or by rosettes; regions of maximum strain can be located and the directions of principal strain can be predicted. The threshold strain of modern lacquers is about 5×10^{-4}.

The first primitive lacquer coats were used as early as 1925 (Sauerwald) and 1934 (Portevin), but wide application, particularly in the elastic strain region, did not start before 1937 (Ellis). There are now several commercial products on the market, such as 'Stresscoat' (Magnaflux, U.S.A.) which comes in fifteen different types of liquid solution for painting or spraying, and a lacquer made by SNECMA, France, which may be in liquid or powder form, the latter being spread by application of heat. There are also some experimental brittle coats in use (Glasurit, Maybach).

1.8.2   *Photoelastic Method*

Stress analysis by photoelastic and X-ray methods are wide subjects in their own right. Strictly, they do not fall under the heading of strain gauges, but in some cases they may be alternative methods of solving a particular stress problem, and some understanding of at least their basic modes of operation should therefore be useful, if not essential, to the strain gauge expert.

Photoelasticity is a model technique; it cannot be employed on the actual structure under investigation * but requires a model to be made up from a transparent material with specific optical and mechanical properties. Its main application is in two-dimensional stress problems, such as notches or holes in bars under bending loads, though investigation of three-dimensional stress patterns is also possible.

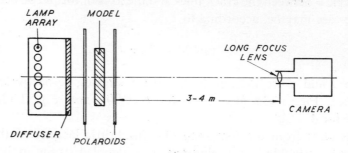

Fig. 1.14 Polariscope without condensers (Hiltscher)

The photoelastic effect (Brewster, 1812) is based on the variation of the propagation velocity of light occurring in many transparent materials exposed to mechanical stress. It is made perceptible by selecting, by means of polarisers, plane-polarised light which, after its passage through the model, is viewed through a second polariser. If the plane of polarisation of this second polariser is displaced by 90° with respect to the first the background of the field of view appears dark, with superimposed light patterns produced by, and accountable to, mechanical stresses in the model. Fig. 1.14 shows a simplified version of a polariscope for use in modern photoelastic stress analysis. The light source is a ground-glass screen uniformly lit from the rear by light bulbs or, for operation with monochromatic light, by an array of fluorescent lamps. The two 'Polaroid' polarisers on either side of the model are also shown, together with a camera at some distance away.

The plane-polarised light arriving at the model surface is split into two independent beams. Their velocities are controlled by the principal stresses σ_1 and σ_2 in the model, tension causing velocity

---

* However, the use of photoelastic layers on the stressed structure (Zandmann, 1959), and of individual slabs (photoelastic strain gauges; Oppel, 1959) have been tried with limited success.

increase and compression decrease. The velocity difference, or retardation, then, is proportional to $\sigma_1 - \sigma_2$, or to the maximum shear stress τ_{max}, and the basic relationship can be written

$$r\lambda = C(\sigma_1 - \sigma_2)d = 2C\tau_{max}d \quad \text{(m)} \tag{1.19}$$

where $r\lambda$ is the relative retardation, in terms of wavelength λ (m), between the two light beams. d (m) is the model thickness and C (m²/N) the photoelastic constant of the model material.

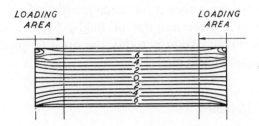

Fig. 1.15 Isochromatic fringe pattern, schematic, of calibration beam under pure bending stress

In monochromatic light distinct dark lines, the so-called *isochromatic fringes*, appear where $r = 1, 2, 3, \ldots$, giving crisp stress patterns well suited to photographic analysis. In white light, because of the range of wavelengths involved, a colour pattern appears which permits analysis also with respect to stress gradients, the colour sequence yellow-red-green-violet indicating increasing stress, and the opposite sequence decreasing stress.

The unit of the photoelastic constant C is the *brewster* ($\equiv 10^{-12}$ m²N); the isochromatic fringe pattern is calibrated by means of a beam of the same model material under pure bending stress. The numbers in Fig. 1.15 show the fringe order, r. Away from the loading areas the fringes should be parallel and equidistant. C is strongly temperature dependent.

A complete pattern of stress trajectories can be obtained from the so-called *isoclinic lines*. However, their plotting requires further experimental sophistication ($\frac{1}{4}$-wave plates and circularly polarised light) which cannot be discussed here.

The *figure of merit* of a particular material is defined as the number of fringes obtainable per unit stress. It should be high in order to avoid excessive model strain which might cause creep and deviation from Hooke's law.

Three-dimensional stress analysis by photoelasticity has been made possible by loading a model at a (moderately) elevated temperature and then allowing it to cool slowly. The strain is thus 'frozen' into the model and, when the latter is cut into slices, a three-dimensional strain pattern can be built up from these (Oppel, 1936).

After Brewster's early and almost forgotten discovery of the photo-elastic effect the subject was revived in 1910 by Coker and applied to stress analysis. Since then it has been greatly refined and is now in universal use in a large number of fields. From a list of several possible choices epoxy resin is today the most frequently employed material for photoelastic models.

1.8.3 X-ray Method

If X-rays incident on a crystalline surface have wavelengths comparable with the atomic spacings in a crystal (order of $1 \text{ Å} = 10^{-10} \text{ m}$) X-ray diffraction occurs and a kind of 'reflection' pattern is obtained (von Laue, 1912) which contains information on the actual atomic spacing. Since the depth of penetration of these rays is very small in metals, only two-dimensional surface strain can thus be measured.

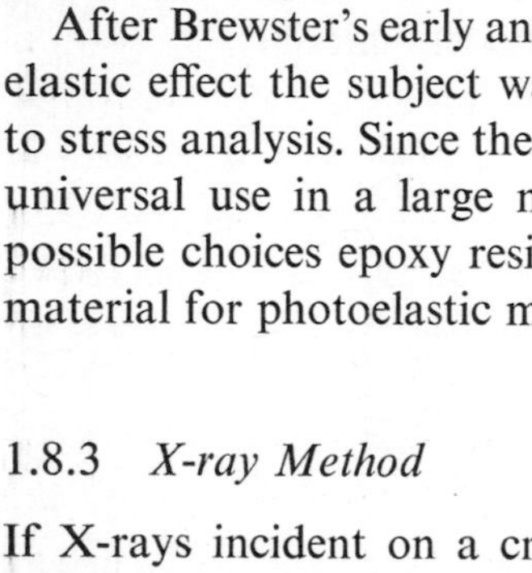

Fig. 1.16 X-rays incident on crystal lattice

Fig. 1.16 shows schematically a (two-dimensional) crystal lattice, the relevant spacing in depth between consecutive atomic layers being d (m). An X-ray beam incident at an angle ϕ produces an interference pattern

$$n\lambda = 2d \sin \phi \quad \text{(m)} \qquad (1.20)$$

where $n \, (= 1, 2, 3, \ldots)$ is the order of the 'reflected' beam and λ (m) the wavelength (Bragg, 1913).

Simple analysis leads only to the sum of the two principal stresses $\sigma_1 + \sigma_2$; it also requires the unstressed atomic spacing d_0, to be known. However, more advanced experimental methods produce individual stress components and eliminate the need for knowing d_0.

Small quantities of gold powder on the test surface are normally used for the calibration of the geometrical set-up for the recording of the diffraction diagrams.

In contrast to mechanical methods of strain measurement X-ray analysis of polycrystalline materials is based on only those crystal orientations that are capable of producing X-ray diffraction, while strain gauges measure average values. There may be significant differences, since in some crystal assemblies the Young's moduli of individual anisotropic monocrystals, such as iron, can differ by more than a factor of two. Also, X-rays might give under identical load conditions smaller strain values, since they measure elastic strain only. Other possible sources of inaccuracy, such as temperature effects and errors caused by a non-uniform stress field below the surface, are usually negligible.

Stress analysis by X-rays is a useful, non-destructive method of high accuracy and, in conjunction with a perforated mask, of high spatial resolution. Specialised X-ray equipment is now available from several commercial sources. A technique for the recording of dynamic X-ray patterns (Schaaber, 1941) by means of a film disc rotating in sympathy with a dynamic parameter, such as time or revolution, does not seem to have survived.

2 Wire Resistance Strain Gauges

In section 1.7.1 on resistance strain gauges we have discussed the historical background and the underlying physical principles of wire strain gauges and we have also compared, in broad terms, their performance and design with those of other types of electrical strain gauges. In this chapter we shall deal in greater detail with their construction, bonding, mechanical and electrical properties and with their associated electrical circuits.

2.1 Construction of Wire Resistance Strain Gauges

2.1.1 *Basic Types*

It may seem strange to the newcomer to strain gauges that a thin wire cemented to a substructure should be capable of taking up tension and, particularly, compression. This will, however, be understood when it is realised that the surface area of a wire of, say, 1 in length and 0·001 in diameter (a common value) is 4000 times larger than its cross-section. This large bonded area controls the movements of the wire almost perfectly and permits no buckling. Under compression the sensitivity of bonded wire resistance strain gauges is in fact lower than under tension by only 1–2%; larger deviations are more probably caused by imperfect bonding between the whole gauge and the substructure.

It will be appreciated that the faithful transmission of strain to the

28

gauge calls for a gauge wire as thin as possible. This also guarantees a high gauge resistance and thus a high voltage output at a given gauge current which, in turn, is limited by the amount of undesirable heat generated in the gauge. A high resistance can, of course, also be obtained from longer wires, and wire resistance strain gauges are therefore arranged in grid form, with as many wires as possible side-by-side. Unfortunately, if the lateral dimension of such a grid is no longer negligible in comparison with its length the gauge becomes sensitive also to transverse strain. A large length/width ratio is therefore desirable but, since the wire spacing is limited by the manufacturing process, the requirement is difficult to reconcile with small gauge lengths, although these need not be known accurately. Figs. 2.1a–f show basic types of wire resistance strain gauges:

(a) The *wrap-around* type is wound on a flattened paper tube or, alternatively, on a thin strip or card. It can easily be made in small gauge lengths and its transverse sensitivity is small, since the loop ends are actually perpendicular to the surface.

(b) The *flat-grid* type is wound in a special jig and then transferred on to the backing. The wire grid is here closer to the substructure than in (a) and gauge instabilities, such as hysteresis and creep (see section 2.2.2A) are therefore less serious. These gauges are also obtainable in 'rosette' patterns for the measurement of two-dimensional strain (see section 4.2), and as temperature-compensated gauges (see section 2.2.2C).

(c) In the *single-wire* type, transverse sensitivity is overcome by soldering thick copper connections to the gauge wires. These gauges are not yet fully proven; they are intended for long gauge lengths only.

(d) The *woven* type has been used for the measurement of large strain, such as on fabrics and on the human skin. They are hardly suitable for engineering applications, though attempts have been made to produce a woven high-temperature gauge with glass-insulated wire in a glass-fibre weave.

(e) The *etched-foil* gauge is produced from thin resistance foil by a photochemical etching process. Because of its larger surface/cross-section ratio (as compared with round wire) it has a higher heat dissipation rate and perhaps better bonding

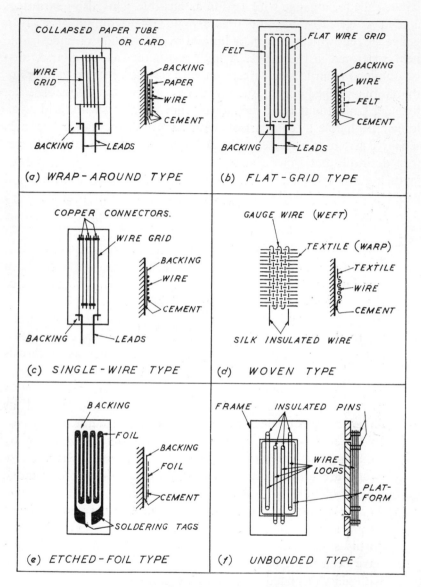

Fig. 2.1 Basic types of wire and foil strain gauges

properties. The transverse sensitivity is low because of the thickened loop ends. In a special process the metal foil, without its backing, can be transferred to the suitably insulated sub-structure and can thus be used at higher temperatures than the conventional organic backing materials would permit. By virtue of the versatile photochemical 'printing' process complex gauge patterns can be produced with ease. These may be gauges for the measurement of shear, arranged in orthogonal arrays and applied at 45° to the axis of a shaft under torsion, and even more complicated patterns for use on diaphragms for the measurement of pressure are feasible. Strain gauge rosettes for two-dimensional strain analysis can also be produced in this fashion.

(*f*) The *unbonded* 'strain gauge' is actually an extensometer. It consists of fine-wire loops wound around insulated pins and arranged so that by a relative movement of platform and frame the tension in two loops is increased and that in the other two decreased. When connected in bridge fashion (Fig. 1.7) they constitute a complete Wheatstone bridge with four active arms. Unbonded strain gauges are used exclusively in trans-ducers for the measurement of physical quantities other than strain (see Chapter 5).

Closely connected with the construction of the wire grid is the attachment of the thicker connecting leads. The connection points (soldered or welded) are often the location of fatigue failures. These may be caused by material changes in the wire due to heating, or simply by stress concentrations due to change of cross-section. Gauge manufacturers have tried various improvements, particularly with gauges intended for high-temperature operation.

2.1.2   *Wire Materials*

Table 2.1 provides a survey of wire materials considered for use in strain gauges. The figures are only average values and may vary markedly with composition and crystal structure (annealed, cold worked, etc.). Some pure metals are also entered for comparison.

The copper–nickel alloys, Constantan, Ferry and Advance, have uniform gauge factors extending well into the plastic range of deformation (see Fig. 1.6c). Their temperature coefficient of resistivity is very low. Corrosion is expected at temperatures above 400°C. Karma has a higher resistivity and corrosion is not effective below 1000°C, but its low temperature coefficient of resistivity is not main-

TABLE 2.1 Properties of Wire Materials for Use in Strain Gauges

ALLOY	NOMINAL COMPOSITION	GAUGE FACTOR	RESISTIVITY (Ω m) $\times 10^{-8}$	TEMPERATURE COEFFICIENT (per °C) $\times 10^{-4}$	ULTIMATE STRENGTH (N/m²) $\times 10^{6}$
Constantan	} 45 Ni, 55 Cu	2·1	48	} ±0·2	} 460
Ferry		2·2	45		
Advance		2·1	45		
Karma	75 Ni, 20 Cr, etc.	2·1	125	0·2	1000
Nichrome	80 Ni, 20 Cr	2·5	100	1	800
Iso-elastic	36 Ni, 8 Cr, 0·5 Mo, etc.	3·6	105	1·75	1250
Alloy 479	92 Pt, 8 W	4·7	62	2·4	2000
Nickel	—	−12	6·5	68	400
Platinum	—	4·8	10	40	200

tained above 150°C. Nichrome and Iso-elastic have somewhat higher gauge factors, but also higher variations with temperature of resistance; the former can be used up to 1200°C and is thus a suitable material for high-temperature transfer foil gauges. Alloy No. 479, because of its high mechanical strength, is used mainly in unbonded strain gauge-type transducers. The excessive (negative) gauge factor of pure nickel applies only over a very narrow initial stress range, as can be seen in Fig. 1.6d.

2.1.3 Backing and Bonding

The backing of wire resistance strain gauges must be stable with time and temperature and must also be compatible with the cement used for bonding the gauge to the test structure. These bonds are permanent, and individual calibration, prior to use, of bonded strain gauges is therefore not possible.

The choice of cement is primarily a question of the maximum operation temperature of the gauges. Table 2.2. summarises the

TABLE 2.2   Summary of Standard Bonding Techniques for Wire
Resistance Strain Gauges

GAUGE BACKING MATERIAL	ADHESIVE	WIRE MATERIAL	REMARKS
Paper or silk	Cellulose/acetone (Durofix)	Copper/ nickel	Useful up to 60°C; up to about 100°C with increased drift
Paper or epoxy type (Araldite)	Epoxy type (Araldite strain gauge cement)	Copper/ nickel	Reduced gauge factor above 50°C; useful up to 150°C
Phenolic (Bakelite) or epoxy type (Araldite)	Phenolic (Bakelite cement) or epoxy type (Araldite 1, 15 or 105)	Copper/ nickel	Requires high bonding pressure. Up to 200°C; for short periods up to 300°C
Glass weave or none (transfer gauge)	Silicone varnish (Atlas paint)	Nickel/ chromium	Up to 400°C; for short periods up to 500°C. Dynamic strain mainly
Glass weave or none (transfer gauge)	Ceramic cements (Fortafix, Allen P1, Brimor, Rockide, etc.)	Nickel/ chromium	Above 400°C, but check insulation resistance and polarisation between gauge and earth. Dynamic strain only

various standard bonding techniques for the general user. They are described in detail in the gauge manufacturers' literature and should closely be adhered to.

Generally, gauge mounting starts with a thorough cleaning process, by mechanical and chemical means, of the bonding area. The cleaned and dried surface should have a mat texture and must be free from dimples and dents. The cement is then evenly spread over the area in a thin layer and the gauge on its backing is applied, and held in position by an even pressure. Next, the cement is dried and cured according to the makers' instructions (time and temperature). In some cases more than one layer may be required, with prescribed baking cycles between their applications. Connecting leads are then soldered to the cured gauge and securely fixed to the test structure along their total length (Fig. 2.2). Finally, gauge continuity and insulation resistance to earth is checked.

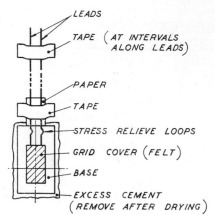

Fig. 2.2 Mounted strain gauge

Special applications in, say, high-temperature environments, or for the measurements of strain at transient and high loads, need extra care. This is also true for bonded strain gauges employed in measurements of high accuracy and long-time stability, such as in load cells and aerodynamic wind-tunnel balances. Particularly in this kind of work the reader should remember these rules:

(*a*) Design for moderate strain levels.
(*b*) Select the longest possible gauge with the highest possible resistance.
(*c*) Follow the prescribed mounting procedure rigidly, particularly with respect to cleaning.
(*d*) Check all soldered joints and connecting leads.
(*e*) Protect gauge assembly from humidity.

This last point can be achieved by coatings of wax, rubber, silicone grease or non-hygroscopic cements, depending on ambient temperatures and convenient modes of application. Note that condensation occurring in an unsealed protection can well do more harm than no protection at all (see section 2.2.2*D*).

2.1.4   *Commercial Wire Resistance Strain Gauges*

It is appropriate to conclude this section on the construction of wire resistance strain gauges by a survey of commercially available types. Because of the vast number of gauge types listed in the makers' catalogues the problem is one of selecting gauges suitable for the general user, without ignoring entirely the more exotic forms for special applications.

Table 2.3 (A) to (H), thus, gives, without regard to cost, wire and foil gauges available in this country from the following British and foreign sources, listed in alphabetic order:

(A) *B.L.H. Strain Gauges*, made by Baldwin–Lima–Hamilton Corp., Waltham 54, Mass., U.S.A. (U.K. Agents: L. Brooke-Edwards, Hove 3, Sussex).

(B) *Philips Strain Gauges*, made by N. V. Philips' Gloeilampen-fabrieken, Eindhoven, Holland (U.K. Agents: M.E.L. Equipment Co. Ltd., London W.C.1).

(C) *A. V. Roe Strain Gauges*, made by Hawker Siddeley Aviation, Ltd., Greengate, Middleton, Manchester.

(D) *Saunders–Roe Strain Gauges*, made by Westland Aircraft Ltd., Saunders–Roe Division, East Cowes, I.o.W.

(E) *Teddington Strain Gauges*, made by Teddington Aircraft Controls, Ltd., Merthyr Tydfil, Glam.

(F) *Tepic Strain Gauges*, made by Physik. Instrumente Huggen-berger, Zürich 10, Switzerland (U.K. Agents: T. C. Howden & Co. Ltd., Leamington Spa, Warwickshire).

(G) *T.M.L. Strain Gauges*, made by Tokyo Sokki Kenkyujo Co. Ltd., Tokyo, Japan (U.K. Agents: Electro-Mechanisms Ltd., Slough, Bucks).

(H) *Tinsley Strain Gauges*, made by H. Tinsley & Co. Ltd., London S.E.25.

The headings of columns 1 to 6 of Table 2.3 should be self-explanatory. Columns 7a and 7b give a rough guide to the maximum operational temperatures for static and dynamic strain measurements. These values, as quoted by the manufacturers, are only approximate and direct comparison between different makes may be unfair to the more cautious manufacturers. (Temperature characteristics of wire

TABLE 2.3 List of Some Commercial Wire and Foil Strain Gauges

(A) B.L.H. Strain Gauges*

1	2	3	4	5	6	7a	7b	8
		GAUGE LENGTH	BASE SIZE	GAUGE FACTOR	RESIST-ANCE	MAXIMUM TEMPERATURE		
						STATIC	DYNAMIC	
TYPE NUMBER	CONSTRUCTION	mm	mm	—	Ω	°C	°C	REMARKS
—	(see Fig. 2.1)							
1 A-19	Wrap-around	1·6	19 × 6·4†	1·7	60	40		Paper base, Constantan
2 A-8	Wrap-around	3·2	19 × 3·2	1·8	120	40		
3 AD-7	Wrap-around	6·4	22 × 5·5	1·9	120	40		
4 AD-3	Flat grid	20·5	51 × 12	2·0	120	65		
5 AB-19	Wrap-around	1·6	16 × 4	1·7	60	120		Bakelite base, Constantan
6 AB-11	Wrap-around	3·2	16 × 5·5	1·9	120	120		
7 AB-14	Wrap-around	9·5	25 × 8·8	2·0	500	120		
8 ABD-3	Flat grid	19	41 × 6·4	2·0	120	120	200	
9 CBD-8	Wrap-around	3·2	22 × 8·8	3·0	500		180	Bakelite base, Iso-elastic
10 CBD-7	Wrap-around	6·4	25 × 5·5	3·2	500		180	
11 C-5-1	Flat grid	12·7	41 × 8·8	3·3	350		80	Paper base, Iso-elastic
12 CX-1	90°-rosette (flat grid)	22	51 × 51	3·5	500		80	
13 ABR-1	90° + 60°-rosette (flat grid)	16	41 × 31	2·1	350	150		Bakelite base, Constantan

TABLE 2.3—*continued.*

(A) B.L.H. Strain Gauges* (continued)

1	2	3	4	5	6	7a	7b	8
		GAUGE LENGTH	BASE SIZE	GAUGE FACTOR	RESIST- ANCE	MAXIMUM TEMPERATURE		
TYPE NUMBER	CONSTRUCTION					STATIC	DYNAMIC	REMARKS
—	(see Fig. 2.1)	mm	mm	—	Ω	°C	°C	
14 AR-4-1	120°-delta (flat grid)	19	38 × 38	2·0	120	65		Paper base, Constantan
15 ABF-11SX	Flat grid	3·2	16 × 4	2·0	120	150		Bakelite base, special alloy (temperature compensated)
16 ABF-7SX	Flat grid	6·4	22 × 6·4	2·0	120	150		
17 AFX-7SX	90°-rosette (flat grid)	6·4	25 × 11	2·0	120	65		Paper base, special alloy (temperature compensated)
18 EBF-7S+	Dual element (flat grid)	6·4	25 × 7·1	2·0	120	150		Temperature compensated for steel (+10°C to +120°C)
19 EBF-7D+	Dual element (flat grid)	6·4	25 × 7·1	2·0	120	150		Temperature compensated for Dural (+10°C to +120°C)
20 HT-1250-8B	Flat grid	12·7	12·7 × 3·6‡	4·0	500	650	800	Transfer gauge, platinum alloy (with thermocouple)
21 FA-03-12SX	Etched foil	1	6·4 × 4·8	2·1	120	95		Epoxy base, Constantan
22 FA-12-50SX	Etched foil	3·1	12·7 × 12	2·1	500	95		
23 FA-25-50SX	Etched foil	6·4	12·7 × 6·4	2·1	500	95		
24 FNH-12-12B	Etched foil	3·1	6·9 × 2·8‡	2·2	120	320	1000	Transfer gauge, Nichrome V
25 FNH-25-12	Etched foil	6·4	11·5 × 4·6‡	2·2	120	320	1000	

* Makers' catalogue lists 233 different types. † Base length × trimmed width, approx. ‡ Grid size, approx.

TABLE 2.3—*continued*

(B) Philips Strain Gauges*

1	2	3	4	5	6	7a	7b	8
		GAUGE LENGTH	BASE SIZE	GAUGE FACTOR	RESIST-ANCE	MAXIMUM TEMPERATURE		
TYPE NUMBER	CONSTRUCTION					STATIC	DYNAMIC	REMARKS
—	(see Fig. 2.1)	mm	mm	—	Ω	°C	°C	
1 PR 9211	Flat grid	12	27 × 8·5	2§	120	40‡	60	Paper base, Cu–Ni alloy
2 PR 9814M	Wrap-around	2	22 × 5	2	300	50	200	
3 PR 9814†	Wrap-around	4	31 × 8·5	2	120	50	200	
4 PR 9812†	Wrap-around	8	35 × 14	2	600	50	200	
5 PR 9811†	Flat grid	12	39 × 8·5	2	120	80	200	
6 PR 9810†	Flat grid	25	52 × 14	2	600	80	200	
7 PR 9815	120°-rosette (flat grid)	12	53 × 53	2	120	80	200	
8 PR 9819	90°-pair (flat grid)	12	30 × 30	2	120	80	200	Cresol base, Cu–Ni alloy
9 PR 9833K/03†	Etched foil	2·5	8·5 × 5	2	120	80	200	
10 PR 9832K/10†	Etched foil	8·3	22 × 8·5	2	600	80	200	
11 PR 9840K/10†	90°-pair (etched foil)	5	14 × 14	2	120	80	200	
12 PR 9846K/12†	120°-rosette (etched foil)	2·5	14 × 14	2	120	80	200	

* Makers' catalogue lists 21 different types,　† Also available with temperature compensation.
‡ About 1% long-time creep.　§ Nominal value.

TABLE 2.3—*continued*

(C) A. V. Roe Strain Gauges*

1	2	3	4	5	6	7a	7b	8
		GAUGE LENGTH	BASE SIZE	GAUGE FACTOR	RESIST-ANCE	MAXIMUM TEMPERATURE		
TYPE NUMBER	CONSTRUCTION					STATIC	DYNAMIC	REMARKS
—	(see Fig. 2.1)	mm	mm	—	Ω	°C	°C	
1 A50	Flat grid	9	15 × 5	2·0	50	80		⎫
2 A100	Flat grid	13	19 × 8	2·0	100	80		⎬ Paper base, Advance
3 A200	Flat grid	20	25 × 9	2·0	200	80		⎭
4 K50	Flat grid	5	10 × 5	2·2	50	80		⎫
5 K250	Flat grid	11	18 × 8	2·2	250	80		⎬ Paper base, Karma
6 KZ8/300	Flat grid	5	11 × 8	2·2	300	80		⎭
7 A100/2	90°-rosette (flat grid)	18	27 × 27	2·0	100	80		⎫ Paper base, Advance
8 A100/3	45°-rosette (flat grid)	18	27 × 27	2·0	100	80		⎭
9 F951C	Single-wire	9	10 × 8	2·2	100		240	⎫ Paper base, Nichrome V
10 S951/2	Single-wire	20†	32 × 2·5	2·2	120		240	⎭
11 RK100H	Single-wire	6	6 × 6	2·2	100	—	1000	⎫ Wire transfer gauges, Nichrome V, special mounting process
12 RK100	Single wire	9	10 × 5	2·2	100	—	1000	⎭

* Makers' catalogue lists 51 different types. All types (except S951/2) can be supplied with integral thermocouples.
† Single strand.

TABLE 2.3—*continued*

(D) Saunders–Roe Strain Gauges*

1	2	3	4	5	6	7a	7b	8
		GAUGE LENGTH	BASE SIZE	GAUGE FACTOR	RESIST-ANCE	MAXIMUM TEMPERATURE STATIC	DYNAMIC	
TYPE NUMBER	CONSTRUCTION							REMARKS
	(see Fig. 2.1)	mm	mm	—	Ω	°C	°C	
1 1/8/LIN	Etched foil	3·2	5·3 × 2·4†	2·0–2·3‡	50–120§	100		
2 1/4/LIN	Etched foil	6·4	10 × 4·5	2·0–2·3‡	50–120§	100		
3 1/2/LIN	Etched foil	12·8	19 × 5·7	2·0–2·3‡	50–120§	100		
4 1/LIN	Etched foil	25·4	34 × 10	2·0–2·3‡	50–120§	100		Epoxy base, Cu–Ni alloy
5 1/4S/LIN	Etched foil	6·4	10 × 4·5	2·0–2·3‡	50–120§		300	
6 1/S/LIN	Etched foil	25·4	34 × 10	2·0–2·3‡	50–120§		300	Transfer gauge, Cu–Ni alloy
7 1/4SN/LIN	Etched foil	6·4	10 × 4·5	2·0–2·3‡	50–75§	—	800	
8 1/SN/LIN	Etched foil	25·4	34 × 10	2·0–2·3‡	150–200§	—	800	Transfer gauge, Ni–Cr alloy
9 1/2 Delta	120°-delta (etched foil)	12·8	30 dia.	2·0–2·3‡	50–120§	100		
10 1/2 Torque	90°-pairs (etched foil)	12·8	8 wide	2·0–2·3‡	50–250§‖	100		Epoxy base, Cu–Ni alloy
11 4ED/Redshaw¶	Diaphragm (etched foil)	—	6·4–64 dia.	2·0–2·3‡	25–50§	100		

* Makers' catalogue lists 27 different types.　† Grid size, approx.　‡ Depending on size.　§ In steps of 5 ohms.
‖ 1 to 5 pairs, 50 ohms each gauge.　¶ Four-arm diaphragm gauge.

TABLE 2.3—*continued*

(E) Teddington Strain Gauges*

TYPE NUMBER	CONSTRUCTION (see Fig. 2.1)	GAUGE LENGTH mm	BASE SIZE mm	GAUGE FACTOR —	RESIST-ANCE Ω	MAXIMUM TEMPERATURE		REMARKS
						STATIC °C	DYNAMIC °C	
1 SE/A/73	Wrap-around	3	32 × 12	1·85	200	100		⎫
2 SE/A/5	Wrap-around	6	41 × 10	1·9	200	100		⎬ Paper base, Eureka
3 SE/A/3	Wrap-around	12·5	41 × 10	2·05	400	100		⎭
4 SE/A/69	Wrap-around	25	60 × 12	2·05	1000	100		
5 SE/A/49	Wrap-around	12·5	41 × 10	2	1000	100		Paper base, Karma
6 SE/A/39	Wrap-around	12·5	41 × 10	2·2	1000	100		Paper base, Nichrome
7 SE/A/45	Wrap-around	12·5	41 × 8	3·1	400	100		Paper base, stainless steel
8 SE/A/99	90°-rosette (wrap-around)	12·5	41 × 41	2·05	120	100		⎫
9 SE/A/95	120°-delta (wrap-around)	12·5	80 dia.	2·05	120	100		⎬ Paper base, Eureka ⎭

* Makers' catalogue lists 116 different types. Types listed above are self-adhesive (cellulose lacquer); untreated gauges are also available.

TABLE 2.3—continued

(F) Tepic Strain Gauges*

1	2	3	4	5	6	7a	7b	8
		GAUGE LENGTH	BASE SIZE	GAUGE FACTOR	RESIST-ANCE	MAXIMUM TEMPERATURE		REMARKS
						STATIC	DYNAMIC	
TYPE NUMBER	CONSTRUCTION	mm	mm	—	Ω	°C	°C	
—	(see Fig. 2.1)							
1 BL½/120	Single-wire	5	12 × 10	2·5	120	80		Transparent lacquer base, Cu–Ni alloy; thermo-setting cement
2 BL1/120	Single-wire	10	17 × 10	2·5	120	80		
3 BL2/600	Single-wire	20	28 × 10	2·5	600	80		
4 BP½/120	Single-wire	5	12 × 10	2·5	120	80		Paper base, Cu–Ni alloy
5 BP1/120	Single-wire	10	17 × 10	2·5	120	80		
6 BP2/600	Single-wire	20	28 × 10	2·5	600	80		
7 CP1/300	Single-wire	10	18 × 10	3·5	300	—	80	Paper base, Invar
8 CP2/500	Single-wire	20	28 × 10	3·5	500	—	80	

* Makers' catalogue lists 33 different types.

TABLE 2.3—*continued*

(G) T.M.L. Strain Gauges*

1	2	3	4	5	6	MAXIMUM TEMPERATURE		8
						7a	7b	
TYPE NUMBER	CONSTRUCTION	GAUGE LENGTH	BASE SIZE	GAUGE FACTOR	RESIST-ANCE	STATIC	DYNAMIC	REMARKS
—	(see Fig. 2.1)	mm	mm	—	Ω	°C	°C	
1 PL-3	Flat grid	3	8 × 4	1·9	120	80	100	
2 PL-10	Flat grid	10	25 × 8	2·1	120	80	100	
3 PC-5	90°-rosette (flat grid)	5	12 × 12	2·05	120	80	100	Polyester sandwich, Cu–Ni alloy
4 PR-5	45°-rosette (flat grid)	5	12 × 12	2·05	120	80	100	
5 HPL-5	Flat grid	5	17 × 7	2·05	120	180	200	
6 HPL-10	Flat grid	10	25 × 8	2·1	120	180	200	
7 PML-30	Flat grid	30	85 × 13 × 5	2·2	120	—	—	For moulding into concrete
8 N-123A	Flat grid	25	40 × 8	2·2	120	330	400	Ceramic base, special cement

* Makers' catalogue lists 51 different types.

TABLE 2.3—*continued*

(H) Tinsley Strain Gauges*

1	2	3	4	5	6	7a	7b	8
		GAUGE LENGTH	BASE SIZE	GAUGE FACTOR	RESISTANCE	MAXIMUM TEMPERATURE		
TYPE NUMBER	CONSTRUCTION					STATIC	DYNAMIC	REMARKS
—	(see Fig. 2.1)	mm	mm	—	Ω	°C	°C	
1 20A	Wrap-around	3	16 × 11	1·7	120	60	100	Paper base, Advance
2 20B	Wrap-around	6	19 × 8	1·8	120	60	100	
3 20C	Wrap-around	10	22 × 13	2·0	340	60	100	
4 6E	Flat grid	16	26 × 11	2·2	100	60	100	
5 5K3	Flat grid	21	35 × 9	2·2	120	60	100	
6 7B	Flat grid	31	48 × 10	2·2	600	60	100	
7 25B	Flat grid	25	41 × 10	3·7	600	60	100	Paper base, Iso-elastic
8 6J	Flat grid	8	13 × 6	2·1	100	—	100	Paper base, Nichrome
9 5B	45°-rosette (flat grid)	16	27 × 27	2·2	100	60	100	Paper base, Advance
10 2V	Wrap-around	2	5 × 2	1·9	120	200	250	Bakelite base, Advance
11 26C	Wrap-around	3	10 × 8	3·1	600	200	250	Bakelite base, Iso-elastic
12 26B	Flat grid	6	9 × 6	3·3	120	200	250	Bakelite base, Iso-elastic
13 28A	Flat grid	7	12 × 9	2·0	600	200	250	Bakelite base, Karma
14 Z½	Flat grid	10	16 × 11	2·2-2·6	1000	400	800	Wire transfer gauges, special mounting process
15 W1	Flat grid	13	16 × 11	2·2-2·6	600	400	800	

* Makers' catalogue lists 67 different types.

resistance strain gauges will be discussed in greater detail in section 2.2.2.) Finally, column 8 contains useful information on the backing and wire materials, and on other special features. Table 2.3 also includes a sprinkling of gauges for two-dimensional strain analysis, such as 90°-shear pairs, rosettes and delta configurations. Types and uses of these compound gauges will be discussed in section 4.2 on stress analysis with strain gauge rosettes.

For a wider choice, more detailed characteristics and recommended methods of handling and mounting gauges the manufacturers' literature should be consulted.

2.2 Properties of Wire Resistance Strain Gauges

2.2.1 *Sensitivity (Gauge Factor)*

In section 1.7.1A the sensitivity, or gauge factor k, of wire resistance strain gauges was given as

$$k = \frac{\Delta R/R}{\Delta l/l} = 1 + 2v + \frac{\Delta\rho/\rho}{\Delta l/l} \tag{2.1}$$

or, with Poisson's ratio $v = 0\cdot3$ for most metals,

$$k = 1\cdot6 + \frac{\Delta\rho/\rho}{\Delta l/l} \tag{2.2}$$

where R (ohm) is the gauge resistance and ΔR (ohm) the resistance variation, caused by a variation Δl (m) of gauge length l (m). The term $(\Delta\rho/\rho)/(\Delta l/l)$ represents a specific change of resistivity ρ (ohm m) which for most wire materials depends on strain (Fig. 1.6). Fortunately, the Constantan-type copper–nickel alloys have a uniform gauge factor at, or near, a value of two which extends well into the region of plastic deformation, and since they have also a very small temperature coefficient of resistivity, the vast majority of general-purpose strain gauges use this type of wire. The most common wire diameter is 0·001 in (0·025 mm), but some gauges are made of thinner wire.

The effective gauge factor of the mounted strain gauge depends also on gauge geometry and on bonding cement and technique. Very short gauges have somewhat lower gauge factors, as can be seen from

Table 2.3. Some wire materials have gauge factors higher than two, but their linear range is limited; they are normally restricted to dynamic measurements where the higher sensitivity may be an over-riding advantage, and to high environmental temperatures (Tables 2.1 and 2.3).

A strictly constant gauge factor assumes a perfectly linear resistance/strain relationship. Well bonded, high-class wire resistance strain gauges satisfy this requirement to a surprisingly high degree; this linearity is, no doubt, their major advantage over semiconductor strain gauges which have vastly higher sensitivities, but basically non-linear calibration curves. Small deviations from linearity caused by hysteresis and creep will be discussed in the section to follow.

The transverse sensitivity of wire and foil strain gauges is usually of little consequence, unless the lateral strain is much larger than that along the gauge. In this case a proper two-dimensional stress analysis with strain rosettes would be indicated, anyway. The contribution from the semicircular ends of flat-grid wire gauges is accessible to analysis which shows that the gauge factor should decrease by about 0·7%, because of lateral contraction. In practice the cross sensitivities of this gauge type vary between +0·3 and +0·4%. In wrap-around and etched foil types the conditions are more complex and the cross sensitivities are usually negative. The single-wire type (Fig. 2.1c) is virtually free from this error.

2.2.2 *Precision*

Under this heading we shall discuss the effects which influence the performance of wire resistance strain gauges. They may be inherent in the gauge materials under static or dynamic strain, such as hysteresis, creep and fatigue, or brought about by the environment of the gauge, such as temperature and humidity variations. The adverse effects of the former group usually depend on the level of strain and are often aggravated by those of the latter. The absolute accuracy of strain measurement by wire resistance strain gauges will be discussed in section 2.2.3.

(*A*) *Hysteresis and Creep.*   Fig. 2.3 shows schematically a typical resistance/strain history of a bonded wire resistance strain gauge.

At the first loading (1) the resistance variation slows down at higher strain values and the complete cycle (1, 2) thus describes a narrow loop, analogous with the well known magnetic hysteresis. At the second (3,4) and later load cycles this performance is repeated, though with reduced deviations. Eventually, a virtually linear characteristic with negligible hysteresis is obtained. The errors shown in Fig. 2.3

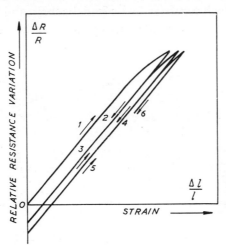

Fig. 2.3 Resistance/strain history, schematic, of a bonded wire resistance
strain gauge (hysteresis loops are exaggerated)

have been exaggerated for clarity; well bonded, high-class strain gauges at room temperatures, and operating within their prescribed level of strain,* have usually negligible hysteresis, even during their first load cycle. It is, however, advisable always to cycle a strain gauge installation a few times at a slightly increased strain level, prior to measurement. Excessively high values of hysteresis found in practical tests are almost invariably due to imperfect bonding.

An interesting use of the normally unwanted effect of gauge hysteresis has recently been made in the so-called *fatigue gauge* (Harting/Bean, 1965). If a special copper–nickel alloy wire with pronounced hysteresis is exposed to fluctuating strain over a period of time, then the accumulative zero-shift of this gauge is a (non-linear) measure of fatigue, since it obviously depends on the energy loss per

* The *elastic* strain limit of well bonded wire and foil gauges is 0·1–0·3%, depending on gauge type.

cycle (hysteresis loop) multiplied by the number of cycles. The reading is said to be repeatable within 10–20% of the total fatigue life.

Hysteresis is independent of time, i.e. strain does not vary with
time at constant load. Any time-dependent strain variation at
constant stress is called *creep*. The physics of hysteresis and creep is
complex, particularly in a compound structure, such as a bonded
strain gauge which consists of wire grid, backing and lead connections,
all held together and bonded to the surface by cement. However,

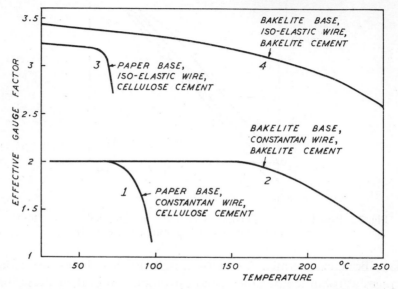

Fig. 2.4 Variation with temperature of gauge factor of some bonded
strain gauges

creep is most obviously affected by temperature; indeed, it actually
sets the temperature limits up to which bonded gauges can usefully
be employed. Fig. 2.4 shows a comparison of typical characteristics
of some common types of gauge constructions. It seems that the
gauge factor variations with temperature, caused by creep, either
remain very small over a relatively short temperature range and then
increase sharply, or there is a more continuous decline of gauge
factor over a wider temperature range. From curve 2 of Fig. 2.4 we
observe that, in spite of its fairly low gauge factor and a somewhat
more elaborate mounting technique, the Constantan wire gauge with
Bakelite base and cement makes a reliable strain sensor for tem-

peratures up to about 200°C; hence its preferential use in strain gauge transducers, such as precision load cells and balances. Similar results have been obtained with epoxy-base gauges and epoxy cements (see Table 2.2). We should mention that, although the curves of Fig. 2.4 are typical, they need not necessarily apply to all gauges of similar construction or mounting method.

Since creep depends on time, its effect is most severe in static measurements; in dynamic tests there may not be sufficient time between load reversals for its full development, and consequently the loss in gauge factor at elevated temperatures will not be quite as serious as shown in Fig. 2.4.

Any large creep values occurring at room temperature are, again, most likely due to imperfect bonding. Sound gauges on first loading below a strain of $e = 10^{-3}$ (m/m) should not creep by more than 0·3–0·5% in 24 hours.

(B) *Fatigue.*   As already mentioned in section 2.1.1 the junction between the wire grid and the thicker connecting leads is the most frequent location of fatigue failures. Their occurrence is rather erratic and cannot be related to certain stress levels or number of stress cycles. On average, some improvement has been obtained by attempts to relieve local stresses and to avoid stress concentrations, the most likely cause of this type of failure.

In some dynamic tests at strain levels of $\pm 0·1\%$ and above an apparent drop in gauge resistance may suddenly occur which should be taken as a warning of imminent failure. Its cause is a gradual detachment of the wire grid from the base which permits the wire to release its initial tension introduced during gauge production. Even the gauge base may gradually be separated from the structure under dynamic load; in a particular test this happened to one out of five Bakelite gauges after 4×10^4 load cycles.

Generally, Iso-elastic grids seem to last much longer than Constantan types and Bakelite gauges longer than paper-base types. After an initially bad start etched-foil gauges are now considered somewhat superior to wire gauges.

The gauge factors of surviving gauges, i.e. of specimens not subject to distinct fatigue failures, are only marginally affected by long-duration dynamic loading. Incidentally, the reader should be reminded here that, although well bonded gauges may survive many load cycles, flopping connection leads will not, unless they have been well secured to the test structure.

(C) Temperature Effects.   The effect of temperature, through creep, on the bonding strength—and thus on effective gauge factor—of strain gauges has been discussed in the previous section. However, temperature variations influence the performance of wire resistance strain gauges also in other ways; in particular the variations in gauge resistance due to temperature changes can easily be of the same magnitude as those caused by strain.

Generally, the relative resistance change $\Delta R/R$ at a strain e and a temperature variation $\Delta\theta = \theta - \theta_0$ can be written as

$$\frac{\Delta R}{R} = ek_0(1 + m\Delta\theta) + (\alpha + k\Delta a)\Delta\theta. \qquad (2.3)$$

In the first term of equation 2.3, k_0 is the conventional gauge factor at room temperature θ_0, and m is its temperature coefficient, which in some wire materials is not even a constant, but may depend on strain. The second term comprises contributions from the thermal co-efficient of resistivity α, and from the product $k\,\Delta a$, where $\Delta a = a_1 - a_2$ is the difference between the coefficients of thermal expansion of the test structure, a_1, and of the gauge wire, a_2 (see Table 2.4). It will be appreciated that, if the substructure expands at a given temperature more than the gauge wire, the latter experiences tensional strain, which contributes to $\Delta R/R$ through the term $k(a_1 - a_2)$. If $a_2 > a_1$, there will be compression in the wire. The temperature error of a bonded resistance strain gauge, therefore, depends not only on the properties of the gauge material but also on that of the test structure, and it should thus be possible, by a suitable combination of materials, to obtain temperature compensation with respect to $\Delta R/R$, so that

$$\alpha + k(a_1 - a_2) = 0. \qquad (2.4)$$

Since in metals α is positive, compensation occurs for $a_2 > a_1$, but in practice the limited choice of basic material combinations would provide only partial reduction of the temperature error. Selected melts of gauge wire materials can, however, go a long way. Another possibility is the use of a series connection of two 'opposing' wire materials, such as Constantan and nickel (*dual gauges*), the latter having a negative gauge factor.

TABLE 2.4   Thermal Coefficients of Linear Expansion (10^6 m/m per degree C) of Some Materials, near Room Temperature

Advance	15	Magnesium	25
Aluminium	23	Marble	3–15
Aluminium bronze	17	Nichrome V	13
Bakelite	30–40	Nickel	13
Brass	19	Nylon	60
Brick	3–9	Perspex	80
Bronze	18	Phosphor bronze	17
Concrete	10–14	Platinum	9
Constantan	16	Porcelain	3–5
Copper	17	Quartz	
Duralumin	23	‖ axis	7
Ebonite	80	⊥ axis	14
Ferry	13	Silica (quartz glass)	0·5
German silver	18	Silver	19
Glass	8–10	Steel, carbon or stainless	11
Glass, Pyrex	3	Stone, natural	4–12
Gold	14	Tin	21
Invar	1	Wood	
Iron	12	fir ‖ grain	4
Iso-elastic	4	fir ⊥ grain	58
Karma	10	oak ‖ grain	5
Lead	29	oak ⊥ grain	54
		Zinc	29

Temperature-compensated gauges have been made on these principles and several types are commercially available for use on certain materials, such as steel, aluminium, titanium and quartz. The improvement of temperature stability, and the effective range of compensation, can be judged from the typical curves of Fig. 2.5 which show apparent, temperature-induced strain plotted against gauge temperature.

On inspection of equation 2.3 a third method seems possible, namely, by setting the first term against the second. If m depends on strain, self-compensation at certain strain levels should be feasible. It is left to the interested reader to work out the appropriate conditions.

Apart from these methods of gauge compensation it is, of course,

also possible to compensate error voltages due to temperature
variation in the gauge circuit by either affecting the bridge voltage,
or by injecting a suitable compensation voltage. In the first case a
temperature-sensitive resistor can be incorporated in the gauge, or
positioned close to it, which is then connected in series with the
bridge supply line; in the second case the voltage output from a
thermocouple can be used for compensation, if the gauge circuit is
operated by d.c. Strain gauges with built-in thermocouples are
commercially available.

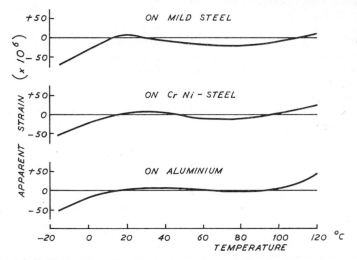

Fig. 2.5 Typical error curves of temperature compensated strain gauges

However, the most common, and the most practical, way of compensating temperature errors in resistance strain gauge installations
is by connecting them, as push–pull pairs, in Wheatstone bridge
circuits; single active gauges can be paired with dummy gauges. We
shall return to this technique in section 2.4, but it may be mentioned
here that only genuine push–pull and bonded dummy gauge arrangements compensate the effects of α *and* Δa; unbonded dummies cannot
affect the Δa-term in equation 2.3. In strain gauge transducers, where
force is measured through stress and strain, any variation with
temperature of Young's modulus of the stressed transducer elements
also remains uncompensated.

The maximum gauge current (*current carrying capacity*) of wire resistance strain gauges depends on the permissible gauge temperature which is controlled by the heat conduction of the gauge and its substructure. Grid pattern, backing material and bonding cement are all of some influence, but the heatsink properties of the test structure to which the gauge is attached is the most decisive factor. Environmental temperature also plays some part. For ordinary wire gauges on paper backings in static tests, recommended gauge currents vary from 5 to 10 mA; in short-duration and dynamic tests 25–35 mA can be tolerated. Bakelite-base gauges can stand about twice this amount. These figures apply to the normal case of metallic substructures; on bad heat conductors (plastics, etc.) wire gauges should not carry more than, say, 5 mA. The current-carrying capacity of etched foil gauges is frequently quoted as the power dissipated per unit grid area. Accepted values on metals are here 1 W/cm^2 for static measurements and 5 W/cm^2 for short-duration and dynamic tests. Because of the higher surface/cross-section ratio of flat conductors, foil gauges should have better heat conduction properties than round-wire gauges.

(*D*) *Humidity*. The first prerequisite for successful moisture-proofing is a thorough drying procedure applied to the gauge assembly. Heat in the form of infra-red radiation should be applied during the whole process of gauge application, since, on cooling due to evaporation, condensation and thus corrosion may occur in the bonding area which, in turn, will cause excessive hysteresis and creep. Generally, residual moisture left in the gauge assembly can produce spurious strain by swelling or contraction of the cement, by loss of insulation resistance within the wire grid and between grid and test structure, and by electrolytic polarisation.

Some moisture-proofing compounds have already been mentioned in section 2.1.3. Most gauge manufacturers offer their own brands of sealing compounds and recommend modes of application. Metal cans and rubber cups, often containing small quantities of silica gel for effective moisture absorption, have also been used for this purpose.

Particular attention should be paid to the joints between the connecting leads; note that most cements do not adhere well to plastic wire insulation materials. Well protected gauge installations

c

can be operated with confidence for several weeks in humid atmospheres, and even under water.

2.2.3 *Accuracy*

The absolute accuracy of strain measurements by means of wire resistance strain gauges is limited by the fact that individual gauges cannot be calibrated prior to use; once bonded they cannot be lifted again without destruction. Mounted gauges can, of course, be calibrated *in situ*. However, this is practicable only on simple structures, where a given load produces a known strain at the point of gauge attachment, as for instance in strain gauge type load cells. In general strain gauging, the strain pattern is usually complex and unknown in detail, and the user must rely on the gauge factor values provided by the gauge manufacturers which have been obtained by 'destructive' calibration of a certain number of gauges per batch.

(*A*) *Uniformity of Gauge Factor*.   Strain gauges are therefore supplied in packages containing five, ten or more gauges of the same kind. Their average gauge factor, together with individual or average resistance values and, occasionally, temperature coefficients of resistance, will be indicated on the package. The scatter of the actual gauge factors of individual gauges in a package varies between ± 1 and $\pm 3\%$, depending on gauge type and manufacturer. Individual resistance tolerances vary between $\pm 0\cdot3$ and $\pm 0\cdot5\%$, unless matched pairs are offered; these may differ by less than $\pm 0\cdot1$ ohm in several hundred ohm.

This information normally satisfies the requirement of the general user of wire resistance strain gauges. He would expect a gauge accuracy of ± 2 to $\pm 3\%$ which will give him an over-all accuracy, comprising all errors of his strain measuring installation, better than $\pm 5\%$ for cautiously designed and carefully executed static measurements, and of about $\pm 10\%$ for dynamic tests conducted under less favourable conditions.

The potential accuracy of wire resistance strain gauges is, however, much better. In order to make full use of their excellent properties the strain gauge specialist will go a long way to secure the best possible results. Many of his efforts will be concerned with electronic instrumentation aspects. We shall discuss some of these in the section to follow, but they cannot improve a basically unsatisfactory gauge performance caused by lack of attention to details in gauge selection, gauge mounting and error compensation. In some sophisticated strain gauge applications, such as on wind-tunnel sting balances, even spatial and temporal temperature gradients, and their effective compensation, may have to be considered; the matching of push–pull pairs may thus require very close tolerances not only for gauge factors and gauge resistances but also for their rates of variation with temperature, in spite of calibration *in situ* being possible in this case.

(B) Calibration.   The number of sample gauges that should be calibrated in each batch in order to establish a reliable average gauge factor depends on the uniformity of the product. With the manufacturing process well established the calibration of 1 or 2% of the total number may suffice. Confidence in the validity of this procedure will be supported by evidence of uniformity in resistance, which can be checked easily for all gauges in a batch. Visual inspection also helps.

Nevertheless, the cautious user may be prepared to sacrifice some gauges and rather do his own calibration, particularly in order to check the proficiency of his bonding method and skill. With the help of an accurate extensometer this can be done at any time on almost any loaded structure. However, the most convenient way of strain gauge calibration under well controlled conditions is perhaps by means of a simple bending beam with four-point loading. In Fig. 2.6 the portion between the two inner supports is subject to a constant bending moment; its neutral axis is the arc of a circle and the uniform strain on the beam surface in this region is

$$e = dt/l^2 \quad (\text{m/m})^* \tag{2.5}$$

where d is the centre deflection measured over a length of $2l$, and $t/2$ the distance of the beam surfaces from the neutral axis. Strictly, the strain e' in the grid of the gauge is slightly higher than on the beam surface, i.e.

$$e = e't/(t + 2h) \tag{2.6}$$

---

* Since strain is dimensionless d, t, l and h can, of course, be measured in any unit of length.

where e is the actual surface strain of equation (2·5), e' the apparent strain measured and h the height of the grid above the beam surface. Usually, $h \ll t$, and the correction can be ignored, except for thick gauges on thin beams and in actual measurements of bending strain in thin strips and sheets.

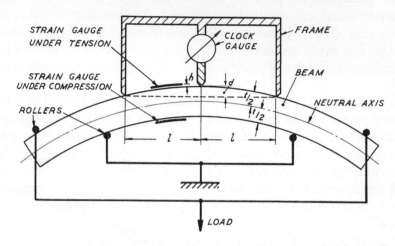

Fig. 2.6 Strain gauge calibrator, schematic

In order to avoid longitudinal stresses due to friction, the beam loading points should consist of rollers and be arranged so that the beam is free from angular twist. The clock gauge in Fig. 2.6, then, measures the deflection d relative to a movable, though rigid, frame of length $2l$. The calibration beam can be removed from the loading mechanism for ease of gauge attachment, drying and curing; it may carry several gauges simultaneously which can be switched from tensional to compressional strain, and vice versa, simply by beam inversion. For tests at elevated temperatures small versions of the apparatus have been used inside an oven, or the beam was heated by passing an electric current through it. The maximum possible strain level at a given temperature is set by the appropriate elastic limit of the beam material. Calibration at higher strain values necessitates the use of mechanical or optical extensometers, discussed in sections 1.3 and 1.4.

2.3   Circuits for Wire Resistance Strain Gauges

2.3.1   *D.C. Operation*

Wheatstone bridge circuits are almost invariably used in strain gauge instrumentation. Potentiometer circuits do not give zero output at zero strain, except in dynamic measurements when a blocking condensor can be inserted, as discussed below. They are also more sensitive to sudden voltage fluctuations than balanced bridge circuits.

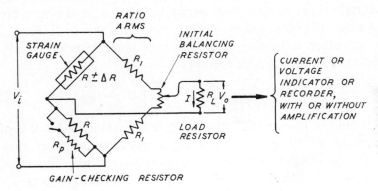

Fig. 2.7 Strain gauge in bridge circuit (out-of-balance method)

If the relative resistance variation

$$\Delta R/R = ke \qquad (2.7)$$

in a strain gauge of resistance R is small, the output current from the bridge at near balance conditions in the load resistance R_L becomes (Fig. 2.7)

$$I = \frac{V_i k e}{2(R + R_1 + 2R_L)} \quad \text{(A)}. \qquad (2.8)$$

R_1 is the resistance of the ratio arms and V_i the d.c. bridge supply voltage. As before, k is the gauge factor and e the applied strain. At large resistance variations the bridge output would not be strictly linear with $\Delta R/R$ (see section 3.3.1).

For $\Delta R/R \ll 1$ the output voltage across R_L is

$$V_o = IR_L = \frac{V_i k e}{2\{2 + (R + R_1)/R_L\}} \quad \text{(V)} \qquad (2.9)$$

and it is seen from equation (2.9) that for $R_L \gg R$ and R_1 (as will be the case when using an amplifier with a high input impedance), the output voltage is independent of R and R_1, namely,

$$V_o = V_i k e / 4 \quad (V). \tag{2.10}$$

For two active strain gauges in push–pull operation the output currents and voltages are twice as high, and for two push–pull pairs (four active gauges) they are doubled again.

A simple check on the operational accuracy of a strain measuring system can be obtained by introducing a known resistance variation at certain times of operation, particularly before and after a test, or test series. If a large resistance R_p is put in parallel to R (Fig. 2.7) or to any other resistance in a bridge or potentiometer circuit, the relative resistance change becomes

$$\frac{\Delta R}{R} = \frac{R}{R_p}\left(1 - \frac{R}{R_p}\right) \approx \frac{R}{R_p}. \tag{2.11}$$

R_p should be chosen such that the resulting value of $\Delta R / R$ is of the magnitude of the appropriate strain range. Note, however, that this method checks the stabilities of supply voltage, bridge circuit, amplifier gain and indicator sensitivity, but not the effective gauge factor.

(A) Static Measurements. (i) Out-of-balance and Null-balancing Operation. In static strain measurements the out-of-balance current of an initially balanced bridge can be read from a galvanometer or recorded by a galvanometer recorder. Likewise, a (digital) voltmeter, a cathode-ray oscilloscope or recorder, with or without a built-in d.c. amplifier, or a self-balancing potentiometer recorder, can be used for the out-of-balance voltage.

In the so-called *null-balancing* method the operator rebalances the bridge at the occurrence of strain and reads its value from a calibrated scale attached to the balance resistor. The operator can, of course, be replaced by a servo loop, shown schematically in Fig. 2.8. The travel of the bridge-balancing servo link, which is a measure of strain, can be recorded in a conventional manner.

The advantages of the null-balancing, as compared with the out-of-balance current or voltage method of Fig. 2.7, are the elimination of errors caused by fluctuations of bridge supply voltage, amplifier gain and indicator sensitivity. Also, matching problems are eased and bridge non-linearities are minimised, because of operation at near-balance conditions. Automatically balanced bridges, such as that of Fig. 2.8, are suitable for the measurement of static or slowly varying (quasi-static) strain only, because of the inertia of the system.

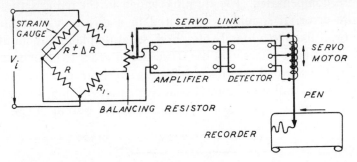

Fig. 2.8 Strain gauge in automatically balanced bridge, schematic (null-balance method)

(*ii*) *Gauge Arrangements.* Although they are not exclusively for static measurements, we shall now examine some basic gauge arrangements with respect to their performance characteristics. The

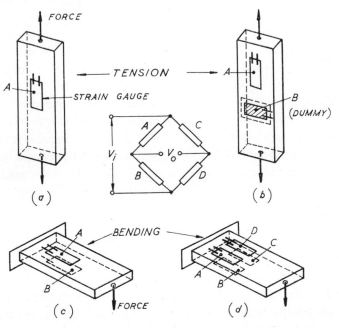

Fig. 2.9 Basic strain gauge arrangements

gauges, or resistors, *A*, *B*, *C*, and *D* of the bridge circuit in Fig. 2.9 can be arranged as follows:

For the measurement of longitudinal stresses (tension and compression) the single gauge in (*a*) has a low output and is not temperature compensated. The dummy gauge in (*b*) reduces the temperature error. It should be mounted in a direction of minimum strain or, if fixed to a loosely attached, separate plate, this should be in good thermal contact with the structure in order to compensate at least for the thermal coefficient of gauge resistance, α (see section 2.2.2C). In a similar fashion, two active gauges *A* and *D*, and two dummies *B* and *C* can be used, giving twice the output of (*b*).

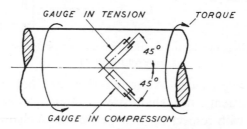

Fig. 2.10 Strain gauges measuring torsion

For bending stresses a push–pull pair (*c*), or two pairs (*d*) are used. These arrangements give maximum temperature compensation; the sensitivity in (*c*) is twice, and that in (*d*) four times, that of a single gauge.

For the measurement of torsional shear strain one can take advantage of the fact that shear in a plane normal to the axis of the shaft is accompanied by tensional and compressional strains in planes at 45° to the axis. The two gauges in Fig. 2.10 operate in push–pull; a second pair could, of course, be added for increased sensitivity. 90°-pairs of wire and foil strain gauges are commercially available (see Table 2.3).

(*iii*) *Lead Arrangements.*   Closely connected with the arrangement of gauges is the lay-out of the connecting leads. Fig. 2.11 shows three possible ways. In (*a*) resistance variations with temperature in the leads connecting an active push–pull pair, or one active and a dummy gauge, are compensated. In (*b*) two leads are in adjacent bridge arms and thus compensated; the third lead in the bridge supply line does not affect bridge balance. For a similar effect a galvanometer lead has been substituted in (c) for the supply lead. The lead resistances should be small compared with the gauge resistances.

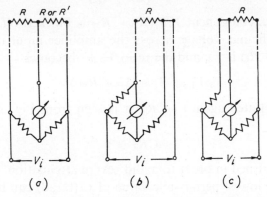

Fig. 2.11 Lead arrangements with temperature compensation
(R = active gauge; R' = dummy gauge)

(B) *Dynamic Measurements.* In combination with a suitable recorder it should in principle be possible to measure any dynamic strain with the circuits described above, if provision is made for the required sensitivity and frequency response of strain gauges, ampli-

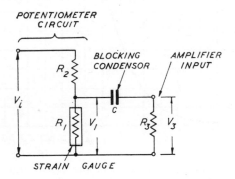

Fig. 2.12 Potentiometer circuit for dynamic strain measurements

fier and recorder. However, an a.c. amplifier of the appropriate frequency range is much simpler and cheaper than a high-stability d.c. amplifier used for static measurements. One might also think of modifying the gauge circuit for dynamic measurements.

Consider the potentiometer circuit of Fig. 2.12. For small

variations in gauge resistance due to dynamic strain the a.c. voltage component V_1 across R_1 is

$$V_1 = \frac{V_i keR_1R_2}{(R_1 + R_2)^2} \qquad (2.12)$$

while the d.c. component $V_i R/(R_1 + R_2)$ is blocked off by the condensor C. The a.c. voltage across the amplifier input resistance R_3 (where $R_3 \gg R_1$) is V_3, and the ratio V_3/V_1 becomes

$$V_3/V_1 = \{1 + (1/\omega CR_3)^2\}^{-1/2}. \qquad (2.13)$$

If V_3/V_1 is plotted against ωCR_3, it is seen from Fig. 2.13 that the condition

$$\omega CR_3 \geqslant 5 \qquad (2.14)$$

should be satisfied in order to avoid severe attenuation. From equation 2.14 the lowest permissible value of C (farad) can be computed for given values of amplifier input resistance R_3, and permissible cut-off frequency $f = \omega/2\pi$ (s^{-1}).

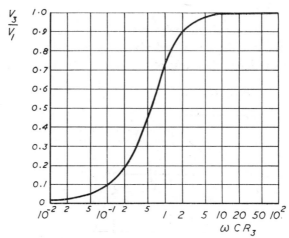

Fig. 2.13 Voltage attenuation V_3/V_1, as a function of time constant CR_3 and frequency $\omega = 2\pi f$

The use of a potentiometer circuit may seem attractive, since no bridge need be balanced and slow resistance variations due to temperature changes are suppressed by C. But the experienced operator knows that sudden, random voltage fluctuations (ΔV) do occur in batteries and power packs. In a potentiometer circuit these appear at the gauge resistance with the large amplitude $\Delta VR_1/(R_1 + R_2)$ and are then transmitted by the blocking condensor because of their high-frequency content. Potentiometer circuits, in spite of their apparent simplicity, are therefore not recommended for use in precision strain gauging.

2.3.2   A.C. Operation

A.C. operation of a strain gauge instrumentation system here means that the bridge supply is an a.c. carrier which is amplitude-modulated by the static or dynamic strain signals. It should not be confused with dynamic measurements with a d.c.-fed bridge discussed in the previous section, although a.c. amplifiers are common to both.

(*A*) *A.C. Bridges.*   A resistor, such as a strain gauge, is normally not purely resistive; particularly at higher frequencies its impedance will have a small reactive component which stems from the self-induct-

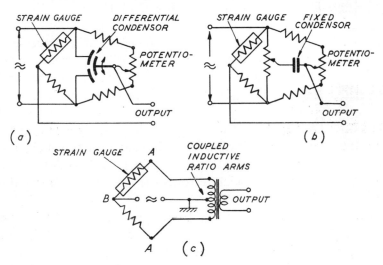

Fig. 2.14 A.C. strain gauge bridges with (*a*) differential condensor, (*b*) fixed condensor and potentiometer, and (*c*) differential transformer output

ances and self-capacities of the gauge grid and the connection leads. A.C.-fed bridges, therefore, require balancing with respect to the resistive (real) and the reactive (imaginary) components of their output. Fig. 2.14 shows two practical ways of balancing an a.c.

bridge. In (a) the potentiometer balances the resistive, and the differential condensor the reactive out-of-balance components separately, while in (b) the two potentiometer settings are not independent of each other. Generally, with strain gauges (in contrast to variable inductance and capacitance transducers) the reactive unbalance is usually small; with identical gauges in push–pull in particular, it can be ignored. In Fig. 2.14c the two resistive ratio arms, R_1, have been replaced by two closely coupled inductances wound in opposite directions on a common core. Analysis of this circuit shows that, since the resulting field of the ratio arms at bridge balance is zero, the points A are virtually at earth potential and stray capacities across the ratio arms, i.e. between the connection leads to the strain gauges and earth, are ineffective. Point B is shunted by the energising source. These properties are particularly advantageous at higher carrier frequencies. In this circuit it is convenient to take the output from a third winding. Since the bridge cannot be balanced initially by adjustment of the fixed ratio arms a small a.c. bias voltage is injected into the output circuit (not shown in Fig. 2.14c).

(B) *Modulation, Amplification and Demodulation.* The processes of modulating, amplifying and demodulating a higher frequency for the purpose of 'carrying' a static or dynamic signal from the strain gauge bridge, can best be understood by looking at Fig. 2.15, which represents a typical a.c.-operated instrumentation set-up for use with strain gauges. At the occurrence of strain the initially balanced a.c.-fed bridge produces an amplitude-modulated output which, after amplification in a conventional a.c. amplifier, is demodulated and filtered in a detector unit which restores the original strain signal on a more convenient output level.

The choice of a suitable carrier frequency is in the first instance determined by the highest signal frequency of the expected dynamic strain. With the limited performance of practical filters in mind the carrier frequency should be chosen 5–10 times higher than the highest component of the signal-frequency spectrum. On the other hand, excessively high carrier frequencies are difficult to handle mainly because of the adverse effects of stray capacities in the electronic circuits and connecting cables; so commercial a.c. strain measuring systems have usually compromised on carrier frequencies of 2–5 kc/s,

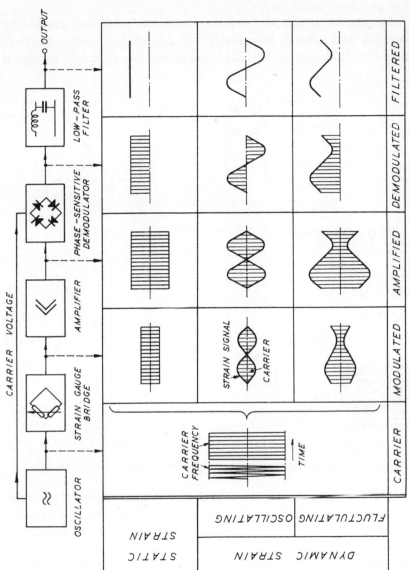

Fig. 2.15 Functional block diagram of carrier system for the measurement of static and dynamic strain

but systems for special applications with high carrier frequencies have also been developed.

The general subject of oscillators and a.c. amplifiers cannot be discussed here, but a few words on demodulators may be both interesting and useful. Fig. 2.16 illustrates the principle of signal

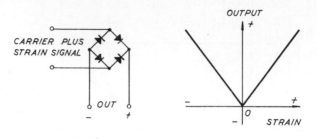

(*a*) FULL-WAVE RECTIFIER-TYPE DEMODULATOR

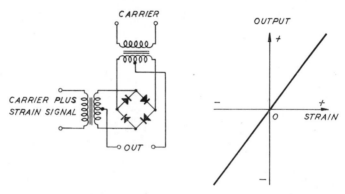

(*b*) PHASE-SENSITIVE RING-TYPE DEMODULATOR

Fig. 2.16 Demodulator circuits and output characteristics, schematic

retrieval (*a*) without and (*b*) with phase discrimination. In (*a*) demodulation is effected by straight-forward full-wave rectification. The demodulator is unaware of the direction of the applied strain (tension or compression), as is shown by its single-sided characteristics. In (*b*) the sign of the strain is retrieved by maintaining the correct phase relationship between modulated carrier and rectifier action. This is achieved by biasing, and thus switching, the rectifiers in the ring-demodulator at the right moments and in the rhythm of the carrier, as shown in the figure. The output characteristic then

3 Semiconductor Strain Gauges

As explained in section 1.7.1*A* the sole reason for the development of the semiconductor strain gauge was the low sensitivity to strain of the metal wire and foil gauges. Since the gauge factor of modern semiconductor strain gauges is higher by a factor of about 50 than that of normal wire gauges, this purpose has no doubt been achieved. But at closer inspection it will be seen that the potential user of semi-conductor strain gauges must pay greater attention to their peculiar properties than with wire gauges.

In this chapter we shall therefore give a brief description of the construction of semiconductor gauge types, followed by a more detailed discussion of their properties. Here a large part of the text will be devoted to methods of compensation for their performance imperfections, such as non-linearity and temperature dependence.

3.1 Construction of Semiconductor Strain Gauges

3.1.1 *Gauge Materials and Manufacture*

In contrast to the polycrystalline metals and alloys of wire and foil gauges, semiconductor gauges are produced from single-crystal silicon or germanium. The majority of gauges are cut from ingots of roughly cylindrical shape, which have been 'grown' in a special process. Prior to cutting, the pure material is 'doped' with the exact amount of foreign impurity atoms (see section 1.7.1*B*) required for the particular purpose. Since the electrical conductivity of the doped material varies with the degree of doping the type of semiconductor material is usually described by its characteristic conductivity, and by the conduction mechanism. Since single crystals are anisotropic (i.e. their physical properties are different in different directions) the orientation of the cut with respect to the crystal axes must also be specified. For example, a common silicon material for general-purpose strain gauges is known as

$$p\text{-type (111) silicon}; \rho_0 = 2 \times 10^{-4} \text{ ohm m}$$

indicating (*a*) conduction by positive (impurity) carriers, (*b*) crystal orientation according to Miller Index (111), and (*c*) room-temperature resistivity $\rho_0 = 2 \times 10^{-4}$ ohm m. We shall discuss the significance of these parameters in section 3.2 on the properties of semiconductor strain gauges.

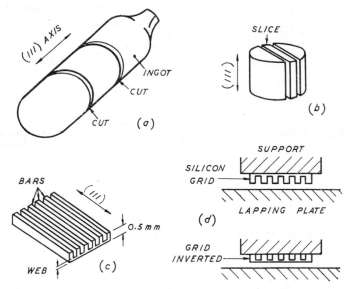

Fig. 3.1 Manufacture of silicon strain gauges, schematic

The process of manufacture of this type of gauge is shown in Fig. 3.1. Since the direction of the ingot axis of silicon is identical with the (111) direction, the length of the first cuts for *p*-type gauges must provide for the intended gauge length (Fig. 3.1*a*). The slices from the second cut are approximately 0·5 mm thick (Fig. 3.1*b*), while the third cutting produces a number of 0·25 mm wide bars or rods, held together by thin webs (Fig. 3.1*c*). In the next step of the procedure first the outer faces of the bars are lapped, then the grid is inverted and the raw gauges are separated by removing the webs in a second lapping process (Fig. 3.1*d*).

The cutting requires great care and experience and is usually done with a special diamond saw and/or with cutting wheels charged with diamond powder.

Since the strength, and thus the smallest permissible curvature in bending, improves with decreasing bar thickness (see section 3.2.4*A*) the latter must be reduced further by a carefully controlled etching process which also smoothes the surfaces. The final product is a filament of about 0·05 mm thickness (cross-sectional area $2·5 \times 10^{-9}$ m²) which is appreciably stronger (see Fig. 3.13), more flexible and therefore less delicate in handling than thicker filaments.

Semiconductor filaments of even smaller cross-section have been produced by condensation of silicon vapour on the cool walls of a quartz tube. These needle-shaped 'whiskers' grow to a length of 5–15 mm with cross-sectional areas of only $2–5 \times 10^{-10}$ m².

The attachment of leads to the semiconductor filament is a delicate job. The lead material is usually gold, doped with a small amount of antimony, in order to avoid rectification effects at the junction. The gold wire is welded to the silicon filament by the passage of a carefully controlled current from two carbon electrodes.

3.1.2 *Basic Gauge Types*

While the manufacturing processes of wire gauges leave room for a variety of gauge configurations (e.g. flat-grid, wrap-around, etc.) all semiconductor strain gauges are basically single-filament gauges and their geometries do not differ much, except for gauge lengths and lead arrangements. The majority of semiconductor gauges in common use have a backing, usually of the phenolic or epoxy type; some gauges are also offered encapsulated in a plastic material. Unbacked gauges, although available in several types, are much more delicate and should be used only sparingly. Some manufacturers also supply gauges bonded to weldable stainless-steel shims.

Fig. 3.2 shows several common semiconductor gauge arrangements. The backed gauges (*a–d*) usually have nickel-plated copper ribbon leads, or printed-circuit type soldering tabs. With the unbacked gauges the gold wires are several centimetres long for ease of handling. The twin pair of Fig. 3.2*d* is a *p*- and *n*-type combination for temperature compensation.

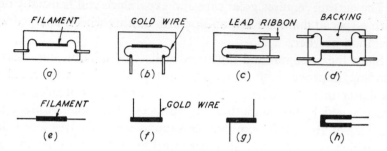

Fig. 3.2 Semiconductor strain gauges
(*a*)–(*d*): with backing
(*e*)–(*h*): without backing

For practical use semiconductor strain gauge types may be classified with respect to the following characteristics:

(*a*) Filament material (almost invariably *p*- or *n*-type silicon).
(*b*) Gauge factor (positive or negative).
(*c*) Gauge length.
(*d*) Gauge resistance.
(*e*) Temperature compensation (if any).
(*f*) Backing or encapsulation (if any).
(*g*) Bonding (cementing or welding).
(*h*) Lead geometry.

3.1.3 *Bonding*

The bonding techniques of backed and encapsulated semiconductor strain gauges do not differ appreciably from those of wire and foil gauges (see section 2.1.3), except for the need of greater care in handling, because of their brittleness. In particular, semiconductor gauges cannot withstand any local pressure from tweezers, etc.

Unbacked gauges are not insulated and therefore require a precoat of cement on the test specimen. They should be manoeuvred into position only by means of their gold wire leads; any direct tweezer pressure is likely to fracture the unprotected filament.

While the lead ribbons of the backed gauges solder and weld easily for the attachment of the longer connecting leads, the gold wires of the unbacked types should preferably be welded, since soldering is tricky. Normal solder embrittles the gold wires, though a 70/30 cadmium–tin solder in combination with a miniature soldering bit and liquid flux has been used quite successfully. The operator should try to gain some experience on a piece of spare gold wire, prior to tackling a complex gauge installation. Generally, the newcomer to semiconductor strain gauges should take the advice, freely offered by the gauge manufacturers, on suitable installation techniques and should follow the prescribed mounting procedure without attempting any apparently easier shortcuts of his own.

3.1.4   *Commercial Semiconductor Strain Gauges*

Table 3.1 lists a number of commercially available semiconductor strain gauges which have been selected from the catalogues of well known gauge manufacturers (listed below) in the same spirit as the wire and foil gauges of Table 2.3.

(A) *B.L.H. Semiconductor Strain Gauges*, made by Baldwin–Lima–Hamilton Corp., Waltham 54, Mass., U.S.A. (U.K. Agents: L. Brooke-Edwards, Hove 3, Essex).

(B) *Ether Semiconductor Strain Gauges*, made by Ether Engineering Ltd., Park Avenue, Bushey, Herts.

(C) *Ferranti Semiconductor Strain Gauges*, made by Ferranti Ltd., Gem Mill, Chadderton, Oldham.

(D) *Kulite Semiconductor Strain Gauges*, made by Kulite Semiconductor Products, Inc., Ridgefield, New Jersey, U.S.A. (U.K. Agents: Electromechanisms Ltd., Slough, Bucks).

(E) *Micro-Systems Semiconductor Strain Gauges*, made by Micro-Systems, Inc., San Gabriel, Calif., U.S.A. (U.K. Agents: Scientific Furnishings Ltd., Poynton, Cheshire).

(F) *Philips Semiconductor Strain Gauges*, made by N. V. Philips Gloeilampen Fabrieken, Eindhoven, Holland (U.K Agents: M.E.L. Equipment Co. Ltd., London, W.C.1).

TABLE 3.1 List of Some Commercial Semiconductor Strain Gauges

(A) B.L.H. Semiconductor Strain Gauges*

	1	2	3	4	5	6
	TYPE NUMBER	CONSTRUCTION	GAUGE FACTOR	GAUGE LENGTH	GAUGE RESISTANCE	REMARKS
	—	(see Fig. 3.2)	—	mm	Ω	
1	SPB1-12-12	Form *a*	+116	3	120	
2	SPB1-20-35	Form *a*	+116	5	350	
3	SPB2-20-35	Form *b*	+116	5	350	
4	SPB3-12-12	Form *c*	+116	3	120	
5	SPB4-17-35	Form *e*	+116	4·3	350	
6	SPB5-10-12	Form *f*	+116	2·5	120	
7	SPB8U-06-12	Form *h*	+116	1·5	120	
8	SNB1-16-35S	Form *a*	−106	4	350	⎫ Zero-shift
9	SNB3-06-12S	Form *c*	−106	1·5	120	⎬ compen-
10	SNB3-16-35S	Form *c*	−110	4	350	⎭ sated
11	SPB2-07-35C	Form *b*	+138	1·8	350	
12	SPB2-12-100C	Form *b*	+138	3	1000	⎫ Gauge-
13	SPB3-07-35C	Form *c*	+135	1·8	350	⎪ factor
14	SPB3-20-100C	Form *c*	+135	5	1000	⎬ compen-
15	SP4-17-100C	Form *e*	+135	4·3	1000	⎪ sated
16	SP5-06-35C	Form *b*	+138	1·5	350	⎭
17	SP5-12-100C	Form *b*	+138	3	1000	
18	SPB3-35-500	Form *c*	+148	9	5000	High resistance

* Makers' catalogue lists 158 different types.

(B) Ether Semiconductor Strain Gauges

	1	2	3	4	5	6
	TYPE NUMBER	CONSTRUCTION	GAUGE FACTOR	GAUGE LENGTH	GAUGE RESISTANCE	REMARKS
	—	(see Fig. 3.2)	—	mm	Ω	
1	2A-1A-120P	Form *a*	+120	5	120	
2	3A-1A-120P	Form *c*	+120	5	120	
3	2A-1A-120N	Form *a*	−100	5	120	
4	3A-1A-120N	Form *c*	−100	5	120	
5	2A-1A-350P	Form *a*	+120	5	350	
6	3A-1A-350P	Form *c*	+120	5	350	
7	2A-1A-350N	Form *a*	−100	5	350	
8	3A-1A-350N	Form *c*	−100	5	350	

TABLE 3.1—*continued*

(C) Ferranti Semiconductor Strain Gauges

	1	2	3	4	5	6
	TYPE NUMBER	CONSTRUCTION	GAUGE FACTOR	GAUGE LENGTH	GAUGE RESISTANCE	REMARKS
	—	(see Fig. 3.2)	—	mm	Ω	
1	ZPG12PE	Form *a*	+130	16*	330	
2	ZPG14PE	Form *a*	+130	16	560	
3	ZPG16PE	Form *a*	+130	16	750	Encapsu-
4	ZPG12NE	Form *a*	−95	16	330	lated
5	ZPG14NE	Form *a*	−95	16	560	
6	ZPG16NE	Form *a*	−95	16	750	
7	ZPG12P	Form *e*	+130	7·6	330	
8	ZPG14P	Form *e*	+130	7·6	560	
9	ZPG16P	Form *e*	+130	7·6	750	
10	ZPG12N	Form *e*	−95	7·6	330	
11	ZPG14N	Form *e*	−95	7·6	560	
12	ZPG16N	Form *e*	−95	7·6	750	

* Over-all length.

(D) Kulite Semiconductor Strain Gauges*

	1	2	3	4	5	6
	TYPE NUMBER	CONSTRUCTION	GAUGE FACTOR	GAUGE LENGTH	GAUGE RESISTANCE	REMARKS
	—	(see Fig. 3.2)	—	mm	Ω	
1	DCP-120-500	Form *a*	+100	6·3	120	Encapsu-
2	DCN-120-500	Form *a*	−100	6·3	120	lated
3	ACP-120-300	Form *e*	+100	6·3	120	
4	ACN-120-300	Form *e*	−100	6·3	120	
5	UCP-120-090	Form *h*	+100	1·5	120	
6	DEP-500-500	Form *a*	+130	6·3	500	Encapsu-
7	DEN-500-500	Form *a*	−120	6·3	500	lated
8	AEP-500-300	Form *a*	+130	6·3	500	
9	AEN-500-300	Form *e*	−120	6·3	500	
10	DGP-1000-500	Form *a*	+155	6·3	1000	Encapsu-
11	DGN-1000-500	Form *a*	−135	6·3	1000	lated
12	AGP-1000-300	Form *e*	+155	6·3	1000	
13	AGN-1000-300	Form *e*	−135	6·3	1000	
14	DHP-10000-500	Form *a*	+175	6·3	10000	Encapsu-lated
15	AHP-10000-500	Form *e*	+175	6·3	10000	
16	MC-EP-120-500	Form *d*	200	6·3	2 × 120	Encapsu-
17	ME-GP-350-500	Form *d*	265	6·3	2 × 350	lated

* Makers' catalogue lists 53 different types.

TABLE 3.1—*continued*

(E) Micro-Systems Semiconductor Strain Gauges*

	1	2	3	4	5	6
	TYPE NUMBER	CONSTRUCTION	GAUGE FACTOR	GAUGE LENGTH	GAUGE RESISTANCE	REMARKS
	—	(see Fig. 3.2)	—	mm	Ω	
1	PA1-05-120	Form a†	+110	1·3	120	
2	PA3-16-120	Form a†	+120	4	120	
3	PA3-16-350	Form a†	+120	4	350	
4	PA3-16-1000	Form a†	+140	4	1000	
5	NA3-16-350	Form a†	−100	4	350	
6	P01-05-120	Form e	+110	1·3	120	
7	P01-16-120	Form e	+120	4	120	
8	P05-16-120	Form h	+110	4	120	
9	P01-16-350	Form e	+120	4	350	
10	P05-16-350	Form h	+120	4	350	
11	P01-16-1000	Form e	+140	4	1000	
12	N01-16-350	Form e	−100	4	350	
13	PE1-16-120	Form h‡	+110	4	120	⎫ Extended
14	PE1-16-350	Form h‡	+120	4	350	⎬ temperature range
15	DCA7-16-350	Form d†	250	4	2 × 350	Zero-shift compensated

* Makers' catalogue lists 39 different types.　† Soldering tabs.　‡ Backed.

(F) Philips Semiconductor Strain Gauges

	1	2	3	4	5	6
	TYPE NUMBER	CONSTRUCTION	GAUGE FACTOR	GAUGE LENGTH	GAUGE RESISTANCE	REMARKS
	—	(see Fig. 3.2)	—	mm	Ω	
1	PR9860	Form c	+160	5	600	
2	PR9861	Form c	+125	5	120	

3.2   Properties of Semiconductor Strain Gauges

3.2.1   *Sensitivity*

In section 1.7.1*B* the gauge factor of semiconductor strain gauges was given as

$$k = \frac{\Delta R/R}{\Delta l/l} = 1 + 2\nu + m \tag{3.1}$$

where $\Delta R/R$ is the specific resistance variation, $\Delta l/l = e$ the strain, ν Poisson's ratio at uniaxial stress, and m the product of piezoresistive coefficient π (m²/N) and Young's modulus E (N/m²) of the semiconductor gauge along its length. The first term on the right-hand side is the contribution from elongation, the second from lateral contraction and the last from the (predominant) piezoresistive effect. However, at higher values of strain, π and thus m and k vary with strain level and, in contrast to wire strain gauges, the resistance/strain relationship is therefore non-linear (see section to follow).

In this section we shall discuss the conditions applicable to low strain levels, where π, E, m, ν and k can be assumed constant; any performance figures quoted here are restricted to this linear regime. We shall also assume constant room temperature throughout ($\approx 300°K$); section 3.2.3 will deal with the effect of temperature variation on sensitivity.

In an entirely anisotropic semiconductor the electric field strength E_e (V/m) is a function of the three-dimensional distributions of current density j (A/m²) and stress σ (N/m²):

$$E_e = E_e(j_1; j_2; j_3; \sigma_{11}; \sigma_{22}; \sigma_{33}; \sigma_{12}; \sigma_{23}; \sigma_{13}) \tag{3.2}$$

where 1, 2 and 3 are the three spatial axes. Equal indices of stress indicate normal stresses, and different indices shear stresses. The general expression for E_e represents a complex tensor relationship, but with the symmetries of the cubic crystal configurations of silicon and germanium—the two most common semiconductor materials— the three-dimensional current density pattern can be represented by

$$E_{e,1}/\rho = j_1\{1 + \pi_{11}\sigma_{11} + \pi_{12}(\sigma_{22} + \sigma_{33})\} + j_2\pi_{44}\sigma_{12} + j_3\pi_{44}\sigma_{13} \tag{3.3a}$$

$$E_{e,2}/\rho = j_2\{1 + \pi_{11}\sigma_{22} + \pi_{12}(\sigma_{11} + \sigma_{33})\} + j_1\pi_{44}\sigma_{12} + j_3\pi_{44}\sigma_{23} \tag{3.3b}$$

$$E_{e,3}/\rho = j_3\{1 + \pi_{11}\sigma_{33} + \pi_{12}(\sigma_{11} + \sigma_{22})\} + j_1\pi_{44}\sigma_{13} + j_2\pi_{44}\sigma_{23} \tag{3.3c}$$

where ρ (Ω m) is the (isotropic) resistivity of the unstressed material, and π_{11}, π_{12}, π_{44} (m²/N) are the relevant piezoresistive coefficients. Typical values for lightly doped p- and n-type silicon and germanium are listed in Table 3.2.

TABLE 3.2　Properties of Lightly Doped Silicon and Germanium at Low Strain Levels and Constant Room Temperature

	UNITS	MULTIPLY BY	p-Si	n-Si	p-Ge	n-Ge
CRYSTAL ORIENTATION	—	—	(111)	(100)	(111)	(111)
YOUNG'S MODULUS	N/m²	10^{10}	18·7	13	15·5	15·5
POISSON'S RATIO	—	—	0·180	0·278	0·156	0·156
UNSTRAINED RESISTIVITY	Ω m	10^{-2}	7·8	11·7	15·0	16·6
π_{11}	m²/N	10^{-10}	$+0\cdot66$	$-10\cdot22$	$-1\cdot06$	$-0\cdot52$
π_{12}	m²/N	10^{-10}	$-0\cdot11$	$+5\cdot34$	$+0\cdot50$	$-0\cdot55$
π_{44}	m²/N	10^{-10}	$+13\cdot81$	$-1\cdot36$	$+9\cdot86$	$-13\cdot87$
m_l	—	—	$+175$	-133	$+102$	-157

The physical meaning of the indices of the piezoresistive coefficient can best be understood by reference to practical cases of current and stress patterns:

(*a*) Current (density) and uniaxial stress along the same crystal axis—

$$E_e/\rho = j(1 + \pi_{11}\sigma). \tag{3.5}$$

(*b*) Current and uniaxial stress along two orthogonal crystal axes—

$$E_e/\rho = j(1 + \pi_{12}\sigma). \tag{3.6}$$

(*c*) Current along one crystal axis, and pure shear stress operating in a plane normal to this axis—

$$E_e/\rho = j \tag{3.7}$$

i.e. no effect on resistance.

(*d*) Shear stress operating in a plane defined by two crystal axes, and current flowing along one of these. Then the effect along the other is—

$$E_e/\rho = j\pi_{44}\tau. \qquad (3.8)$$

(*e*) At hydraulic pressure p (N/m²) we have—

$$E_e/\rho = j\{1 + p(\pi_{11} + 2\pi_{12})\}. \qquad (3.9)$$

In practical semiconductor strain gauges both the stress and current are along the length of the gauge; though this direction may not be a crystal axis. The effective longitudinal coefficient π_l can then be computed from

$$\pi_l = \pi_{11} + 2(\pi_{12} - \pi_{11} + \pi_{44})(n_1^2 n_2^2 + n_2^2 n_3^2 + n_3^2 n_1^2) \qquad (3.10)$$

where n_1, n_2 and n_3 are the direction cosines of π_l with respect to the crystal axes. Since $n_1^2 n_2^2 + n_2^2 n_3^2 + n_3^2 n_1^2$ has a maximum for $n_1 = n_2 = n_3 = 1/\sqrt{3}$, this means that for $\pi_{12} - \pi_{11} + \pi_{44} > 0$ the maximum piezoresistive effect occurs along a crystal direction designated (111), as shown in Fig. 3.3. For $\pi_{12} - \pi_{11} + \pi_{44} < 0$ the maximum occurs along a crystal axis, e.g. (100). Fig. 3.4 shows the gauge factors of *p*- and *n*-doped silicon as a function of resistivity (degree of doping). It is seen that *p*-type silicon (and also *n*- and *p*-type germanium) has its maximum sensitivity in the (111) crystal direction, while *n*-type silicon is most sensitive in the (100) direction.

Like the piezoresistive properties, the elastic properties of anisotropic crystals are also different in different directions. These points will be discussed in greater detail in Chapter 4.

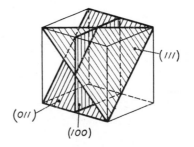

Fig. 3.3 Miller indices of cubic crystal planes, e.g. silicon and germanium

Values of Young's moduli and Poisson's ratios for the relevant crystal directions of silicon and germanium can be found in Table 3.2.

For a semiconductor strain gauge at a strain e, and with longitudinal piezoresistive coefficient π_l (equation 3.10) and longitudinal Young's modulus E_l, the current density in the gauge becomes

$$E_e/\rho = j(1 + \pi_l E_l e) = j(1 + m_l e). \qquad (3.11)$$

With a gauge length l (m) and a gauge cross-section a (m^2) the voltage across the gauge resistance is $V = E_e l$ and the current through it $I = ja$. Therefore, the resistance $R = V/I$ (ohm) becomes

$$R = \frac{\rho l}{a}(1 + m_l e) \tag{3.12}$$

and the specific resistance change caused by uniaxial stress in the gauge is

$$\Delta R/R = (1 + 2v_l + m_l)e \tag{3.13}$$

where v_l is the value of Poisson's ratio for longitudinal uniaxial stress. The sensitivity of semiconductor strain gauges at low strain levels and room temperature can now be computed from equation 3.13, which is identical with equation 3.1.

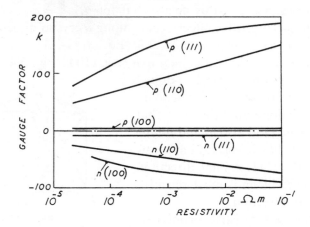

Fig. 3.4 Variation of gauge factor of p- and n-type silicon as a function of resistivity and crystal orientation

Since the values of m_l in Table 3.2 are well in excess of 100, it is obvious that the contributions from gauge geometry (first and second terms in equation 3.13) are insignificant in comparison with the piezo-resistive effect. We therefore conclude that semiconductor strain gauges are vastly more sensitive than wire resistance gauges with gauge factor values around two. Fig. 3.4 shows that this still holds for heavily doped materials of much lower resistivities than those of Table 3.2, which will be discussed in the sections to follow.

3.2.2 *Linearity*

In contrast to wire and foil gauges the sensitivity of semiconductor strain gauges depends strongly on strain level, i.e. semiconductor gauges are distinctly non-linear. We can write the relative resistance change at constant temperature in the general form—

$$\Delta R/R_0 = C_1 e + C_2 e^2 + C_3 e^3 + \ldots \qquad (3.14)$$

where C_1, C_2, C_3, . . ., are constants, R_0 is the unstrained gauge resistance and $e = \Delta l/l$ the strain. However, at normal strain levels the

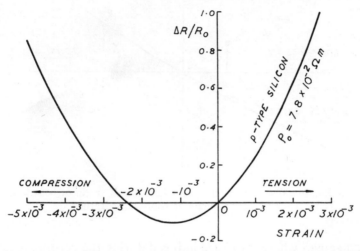

Fig. 3.5 Relative resistance change as a function of strain of lightly doped *p*-type silicon at room temperature

contribution from the strain-cubed term will be less than 1% and can thus be neglected. Equation 3.14 is therefore represented by the parabola of Fig. 3.5 with the minimum at

$$x_m = -C_1/2C_2, \qquad y_m = -C_1^2/4C_2. \qquad (3.15)$$

The lightly doped *p*-type silicon of Table 3.2, for instance, at room temperature obeys the expression

$$\Delta R/R_0 = +175e + 72625e^2, \qquad (3.16)$$

where $C_1 = +175$ is the slope of the tangent of the curve at zero strain. This basic gauge factor applies at vanishing strain only, i.e.

$$k = \Delta R/R_0 e \qquad \text{for } e \to 0. \qquad (3.17)$$

At finite strains the square term in equation 3.16 comes into play, so that if one would start from a resistance other than R_0 for unstrained gauge conditions, the slope at that point of the curve (i.e. the gauge factor) would be different; the unwarranted use of R_0 would lead to errors. Even severe errors of this kind may happen in practice with

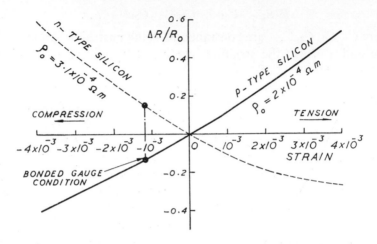

Fig. 3.6 Relative resistance change as a function of strain of heavily doped
p- and *n*-type silicon at room temperature

bonded gauges where shrinkage induced during the curing process of the bonding cement has put a compressional strain bias into the mounted gauge. In order to reduce these errors caused by non-linearity, semiconductor strain gauges are now produced from *heavily doped* materials of low resistivity. As an example, the solid line in Fig. 3.6 shows an experimental calibration curve of a *p*-doped silicon gauge with a resistivity $\rho = 2 \times 10^{-4}\ \Omega$ m. In comparison with equation 3.16 we have here the less non-linear relationship

$$\Delta R/R_0 = +119 \cdot 5e + 4000e^2. \tag{3.18}$$

Note that at the point of bonded gauge condition, marked in the figure, the sensitivity is still lower than at zero strain, though there is a distinct improvement with respect to linearity of the heavily doped material at similar strain levels.

The dotted curve in Fig. 3.6 shows the calibration of an n-type silicon gauge of resistivity $\rho = 3 \cdot 1 \times 10^{-4}\ \Omega$ m, where

$$\Delta R/R_0 = -110e + 10{,}000e^2. \qquad (3.19)$$

The p- and n-type curves are approximate mirror images; in the n-type gauge compressional bonding bias now shifts the working point into a region of higher sensitivity.

A somewhat naïve, though widely practised 'correction' for the gauge factor shift caused by bonding shrinkage, consists of multiplying the gauge factor of the unstressed gauge by the ratio of the unstressed resistance R_0 (both quoted by the manufacturers on the gauge packet) to the measured resistance of the bonded gauge. This method ignores the true character of the parabola and leads to large errors in most instances. Accurate, though more elaborate, adjustments of gauge factors can be made by means of correction tables or curves which take non-linearity (and temperature variations) fully into account. They are, or should be, supplied by all manufacturers of semiconductor strain gauges.

Non-linearity compensation by circuit artifices will be discussed in section 3.3.2 on semiconductor strain gauge circuits.

3.2.3   *Temperature Effects*

Environmental temperature changes affect the resistance and the sensitivity of semiconductor strain gauges to an extent which in a particular material depends on the kind and level of doping (resistivity). As in wire and foil gauges, the 'unstrained' gauge resistance is also affected by the differential thermal expansion of gauge and test structure (see section 2.2.2C) and by strains induced in the bonding process, as explained in the previous section.

(A) Gauge Resistance.   Fig. 3.7 shows the resistance variations ΔR_θ at various temperatures θ (°C) with respect to room temperature resistance R_0 of unbonded silicon gauges with different room-temperature resistivities ρ_0. At low degrees of doping (i.e. at high resistivities) the temperature coefficients $\Delta R_\theta/R_0$ are large, but for heavily doped p- and n-type silicon gauges at resistivity levels below,

say, 2×10^{-4} ohm m, the resistance variation between room temperature and 200°C is less than 20%.

The attentive reader will have noticed that the temperature co-

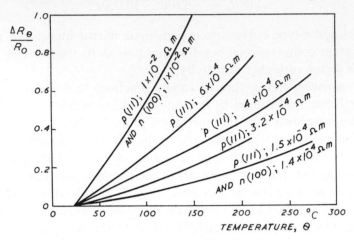

Fig. 3.7 Relative resistance variation with temperature of *p*- and *n*-type silicon of various room-temperature resistivities

efficient of resistivity of doped silicon in Fig. 3.7 is seen to be positive, while the conduction mechanism in intrinsic, i.e. pure semiconductors would lead one to predict a negative temperature coefficient (see

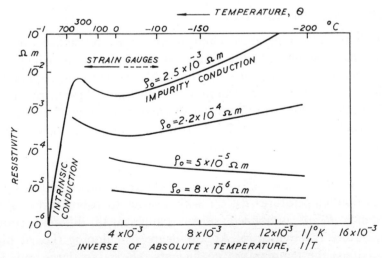

Fig. 3.8 Resistivity as a function of the inverse of absolute temperature of *n*-type silicon of various room-temperature resistivities

section 1.7.1). In fact, the positive coefficient applies only in a limited temperature range. Fig. 3.8 shows a much wider range and it is seen that at temperatures below 0°C the slope is generally negative; at temperatures in excess of 300°–400°C (i.e. well above the operational range of semiconductor strain gauges) it follows indeed the '$1/T$' law of intrinsic semiconductor materials.

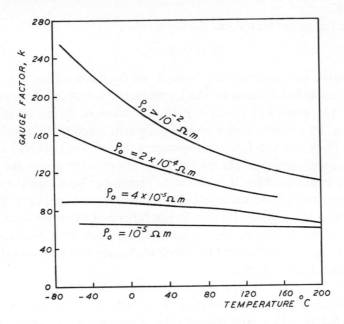

Fig. 3.9 Variation with temperature of gauge factor of p-type silicon of various room-temperature resistivities

(*B*) *Gauge Factor.*   Fig. 3.9 shows the variation with temperature of (unbonded) gauge factor $k = (\Delta R/R_0)/e$ for p-type silicon at different degrees of doping (resistivity). The temperature coefficient of gauge factor is negative and—like that of resistivity—decreases with increasing amount of doping. At very high degrees of doping, i.e. with room-temperature resistivities at and below 10^{-5} ohm m, the gauge factor would be virtually independent of temperature, but strain gauge manufacture with this highly doped material is difficult,* and

* Some highly doped gauges with reduced temperature sensitivity and improved linearity have recently been offered by Kulite; their gauge factor is around +50.

   D

the majority of commercial semiconductor strain gauges are made from p- and n-type silicon doped with about 5×10^{24} impurity atoms per m^3, thus exhibiting room-temperature resistivities around 2×10^{-4} ohm m. The room-temperature gauge factor of the most common p-type gauge is around $+120$ (as compared with $+175$ for the lightly doped material of Table 3.2) which drops to about $+90$ at 200°C.

Since the gauge factor has the form

$$k = \Delta R_e / R_0 e \qquad (3.20)$$

its variation with temperature depends on (a) the temperature variation of resistance R_0, and (b) the temperature variation of resistance change ΔR_e, caused by strain e. If the variation in R_0 can be eliminated (e.g. by operation in a constant-current circuit) the sensitivity $\Delta R_e / e$ will be less affected by temperature than k. On the other hand, suitable combination of the two effects may provide means for temperature compensation. It is useful to remember here that there are semiconductor gauge materials with positive and negative gauge factors which are generally non-linear functions of strain level, and that the output from strain gauge circuits, such as a Wheatstone bridge, are also non-linear at the large resistance variations produced by semiconductor gauges.

The problem of temperature compensation of semiconductor gauges is obviously more complex than that of wire and foil gauges (section 2.2.2C). However, from the large magnitudes of temperature errors in the performance of uncompensated semiconductor strain gauges (see also section 3.4) it is apparent that efficient temperature compensation is their only hope of survival as useful and accurate measuring instruments. Therefore, the maximum operational temperature range of semiconductor gauges is set by the temperature limits up to which reasonable accuracy can be achieved. A range of $-40°$ to $+100°C$ is often accepted in this respect; without regard to temperature compensation common gauge bonding techniques would permit a range of, say $-80°$ to $+250°C$. In contrast to metal gauges the silicon filament proper has no plastic strain region below 500°C and therefore no hysteresis or creep problems.

(*C*) *Temperature Compensation*. It is convenient to distinguish between

    (*i*) self-compensation, and
    (*ii*) circuit compensation.

The first method is effective over a limited temperature range and employs select-material gauges; the second comprises the use of push–pull and dummy gauges, *p–n* combinations, temperature-sensitive resistors (thermistors) and other circuit artifices.

(*i*) *Self-compensation*. The basic idea of temperature compensation of bonded strain gauges with respect to differential thermal expansion of gauge filament and test structure has been explained in section 2.2.2*C* and need not be repeated here. The interesting difference between semiconductor and wire gauges is the possibility of using in the present case *n*-type silicon gauges with negative gauge factors. In fact, the most common *p*-type silicon gauge does not lend itself to effective self-compensation, since its temperature coefficient of resistance is positive and its thermal expansion coefficient is very low ($\approx 2 \cdot 5 \times 10^{-6}$ per degree C).

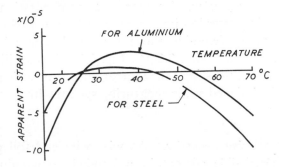

Fig. 3.10 Typical curves of apparent strain in temperature-compensated *n*-type silicon strain gauges for use on aluminium and steel

    Although the temperature coefficient of resistivity of *n*-type silicon is also positive, its negative gauge factor permits effective compensation at temperatures up to about 70°C. Fig. 3.10 shows typical error curves of apparent strain caused by temperature effects in *n*-type silicon gauges bonded to aluminium and steel.

    In single-gauge installations this self-compensating gauge type is economical in use; the mounting process is identical to that of standard p-type gauges and normal constant-voltage bridge circuits (or constant-current circuits) can be employed. Also, since their strain non-linearity is opposing that of a Wheatstone bridge circuit at large resistance variations, good linearity of output can often be achieved.

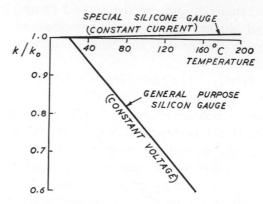

Fig. 3.11 Gauge factor variation with temperature of silicon strain gauges in constant-current and constant-voltage operation

(*ii*) *Circuit Compensation.* Temperature compensation of semi-conductor strain gauges by circuit artifices will be discussed in section 3.3.3. They partly resemble those employed with wire and foil gauges, described in section 2.2.2C. Fig. 3.11 gives an illustration—and a warning—of the size of the temperature error which may occur in a carelessly designed strain measuring system with semiconductor strain gauges.

(*D*) *Current-carrying Capacity.* As with wire and foil gauges, the maximum permissible current in a bonded semiconductor strain gauge is controlled by the mechanism of heat dissipation, mainly conduction to the test structure. On a good heatsink a typical semi-conductor gauge could dissipate a power of more than 1 W without failure or burn-out, but self-heating would seriously impair the stability of gauge resistance and gauge factor. Fig. 3.12 shows the variation of these parameters for a standard gauge bonded to aluminium at various values of power dissipation, related to conditions at 0·01 W dissipation. It is seen that the deviations are not too serious up to about 0·1 W. The safe gauge current of a typical normal-size gauge of 120 ohms is therefore about 30 mA, but short gauges should be allowed only about half this current. For gauges bonded to bad heat conductors, such as plastics, much lower values are recommended.

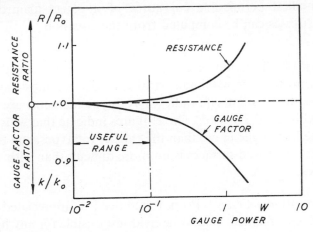

Fig. 3.12 Gauge resistance and gauge factor variations with power dissipation of typical silicon strain gauge, referred to conditions at 10^{-2} W dissipation

3.2.4 *Mechanical Properties*

(*A*) *Breaking Strength and Radius of Curvature.*   At temperatures below 500°C the stress/strain curve of silicon filaments is linear up to the fracture point; there is no plastic range. The breaking stress of silicon depends on filament cross-section (see Fig. 3.13). For

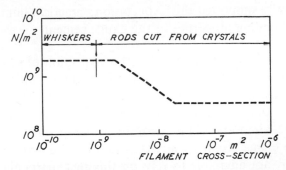

Fig. 3.13 Average breaking stress at room temperature of silicon filaments of various cross-sections

gauges cut from solid crystals fracture occurs at about 3×10^8 N/m² and the related safe maximum strain is 1–$1 \cdot 5 \times 10^{-3}$ m/m. The much thinner gauge filaments made from 'whiskers' (see section 3.1.1) have breaking stresses of about 2×10^9 N/m², with safe maximum strain values of, say, 4–5×10^{-3} m/m.

The smallest permissible curvature of a gauge filament under bending stresses can be computed from the equation

$$r = t/2e \qquad (3.21)$$

where r (m) is the radius of curvature, t (m) the filament thickness, and e (m/m) the safe maximum strain. Under the most favourable conditions the smallest safe radii for rod-type filaments are 7–8 cm, and for whiskers $0 \cdot 3$–$0 \cdot 5$ cm. These figures indicate that whisker-type gauges are less fragile in use than the thicker rod types, and that their attachment to curved surfaces is no more difficult than with wire and foil gauges.

(*B*) *Hysteresis and Creep.* From the above it is appreciated that the semiconductor filament cannot be held responsible for any hysteresis or creep errors experienced in practical gauge installations. Any such effects are clearly a function of the less perfect gauge backing (if any) and the cement, particularly with respect to the maximum operational temperature of bonded gauges. The reader is therefore referred to section 2.2.2 on the properties of bonded wire and foil gauges.

(*C*) *Fatigue.* In view of the perfectly elastic deformation of the silicon filament the fatigue life of semiconductor gauges should be higher than that of wire and foil gauges. Experimental investigations have generally supported this expectation; practical limits are again set by the bonding properties of the gauge cement.

(*D*) *Humidity.* The techniques for the protection of semiconductor strain gauges from environmental humidity do not differ from those in common use with wire gauges (section 2.2.2*D*). Drift from moisture absorption, and noise generated by imperfect insulation of lead wires, are less important in semiconductor strain gauges—because of their much higher strain sensitivity—than in wire and foil gauges. It is, however, not advisable to rely on this fact, particularly if small strains must be measured.

3.2.5　*Miscellaneous Properties*

(*A*) *Temperature Sensors.*　The undesirable dependence of resistance on temperature in silicon strain gauges can, of course, be gainfully employed in a temperature sensor. These instruments are commercially available; by suitable choice of doping level and crystal orientation they have a fairly constant temperature coefficient of about 1% per degree C over a temperature range of $-70°$ to $+200°C$, and a low strain sensitivity. In contrast to thermistors, their resistance/temperature characteristics are essentially linear.

(*B*) *Current Sensitivity of Resistance.*　The resistance of wire gauges is independent of gauge current. In semiconductor gauges a small apparent strain (maximum 5×10^{-7} m/m) has been observed which seems to depend on the magnitude and direction (rectification effect?) of the gauge current, even at very low rates of self-heating.

(*C*) *Thermo-voltages.*　Temperature gradients along the gauge may cause thermo-voltages of order of magnitude 1 mV per degree C near room temperature. As with wire gauges, a.c. operation would eliminate this error source.

(*D*) *Photoelectric Sensitivity.*　The apparent strain produced in an unprotected semiconductor strain gauge filament between total darkness and average daylight may amount to 2×10^{-6} m/m. In high-precision measurements fluctuating light should therefore be prevented from reaching the gauge.

(*E*) *Noise.*　In wire and foil gauges there is only thermal, or Johnson, noise. It is produced by the random motion of free electrons in the conductor which are in thermal equilibrium with the molecules, and its power is proportional to absolute gauge temperature, gauge resistance and transmitted frequency band. The equivalent noise voltage across the gauge is usually negligible, except perhaps in cases of attempting to measure by means of high-resistance gauges very low values of dynamic strain at high environmental temperatures.

　In semiconductor strain gauges there is an additional noise which, in *p*-type silicon for instance, is thought to be related to the life times

of the minority carriers, i.e. electrons, before they combine with holes or produce heat (see section 1.7.1). The power of this so-called current, or excess, noise is proportional to the square of the current and inversely proportional to frequency, down to very low values of frequency. At normal gauge currents (see section 3.2.3D) the current noise will somewhat exceed the thermal noise contribution, though the combined thermal and current noise voltage in a standard semi-conductor gauge at low frequencies and near room temperature should not be greater than $0.1\ \mu V$, which is equivalent to a strain level of less than 10^{-9} m/m.

3.3 Circuits for Semiconductor Strain Gauges

The choice of a suitable circuit for use with semiconductor strain gauges is less straightforward than for wire and foil gauges. The main problems stem from their major advantage: much higher sensitivity. For instance, the output from a semiconductor strain gauge with constant-voltage excitation—the common arrangement with wire gauges—may amount to several volts and can no longer be considered linear with resistance variation. Furthermore, because of the inherent non-linearity with strain of gauge factor, and of variation with temperature of gauge factor and gauge resistance, semiconductor strain gauge circuits are usually designed to provide also compensation for these detrimental effects.

In this section we shall, therefore, first discuss the non-linearities of Wheatstone bridge circuits at large resistance variations, followed by methods for the compensation of gauge non-linearity and of temperature-induced errors.

3.3.1 *Bridge Non-linearity*

The initially balanced (i.e. $R_1 R_3 = R_2 R_4$) bridge of Fig. 3.14a has one active gauge, R_1. The bridge output voltage V_0 at a finite resistance change is given by

$$V_0 = V_i \left\{ \frac{\Delta R_1}{1 + [\Delta R_1/(R_1 + R_4)]} \cdot \frac{R_3}{(R_1 + R_4)(R_2 + R_3)} \right\} \quad (3.22)$$

where V_i is the constant input voltage to the bridge. For a bridge arrangement with equal resistances, i.e. $R_1 = R_2 = R_3 = R_4 = R$, equation 3.22 simplifies to

$$\frac{V_0}{V_i} = \frac{\frac{1}{2}\Delta R/R}{2 + \Delta R/R}.$$ (3.23)

With semiconductor strain gauges this may lead to non-linearities as high as 10–20%. These large deviations from linearity can, however, be reduced if the two resistances R_3 and R_4 are both made larger by a

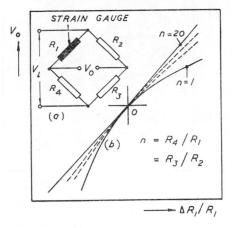

Fig. 3.14 Non-linearity of bridge circuit for various values of ratio-arm resistance ratio, schematic

factor n than the resistances R_1 and R_2. Fig. 3.14*b* shows a gradual improvement of linearity with increasing factor n, assuming for simplicity a linear gauge response. For instance, at $n = 10$ non-linearity is reduced to about 10% of its original value.

3.3.2   *Compensation of Non-linearity*

(*A*) *Bridge Non-linearity.*   It was shown in section 3.2.2 that the (non-linear) calibration curve of *p*-type silicon gauges can be written generally

$$\Delta R/R = C_1 e + C_2 e^2$$ (3.24)

where C_1 and C_2 are constants and e the strain, while the (non-linear) output from the bridge has the form (equation 3.22)

$$V_0 = \text{constant} \times \frac{\Delta R_1}{1 + \Delta R_1/(R_1 + R_4)}.$$ (3.25)

*

Therefore, since the non-linearity of this gauge type (e.g. Fig. 3.6) and that of the Wheatstone bridge circuit (Fig. 3.14b) 'bulge' in opposite directions, good compensation can be achieved by a suitable choice of the factor n, introduced in section 3.3.1. Note that the input voltage to the bridge must be re-adjusted in order to maintain the optimum bridge current.

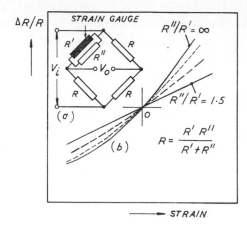

Fig. 3.15 Linearity compensation with shunt resistance, schematic

(*B*) *Shunt Resistance.* Fig. 3.15a shows a bridge with a resistance R'' in parallel to the gauge resistance R', where $R = R'R''/(R' + R'')$. The linearity of this circuit (Fig. 3.15b) is improved at small R''/R'-ratios, but loss in sensitivity is severe, for instance 44% at $R''/R' = 1.5$.

(*C*) *Push–pull Gauges.* Appreciable, though not complete, compensation of gauge non-linearity can be achieved with two push–pull gauges (in tension and compression, respectively) connected to adjacent bridge arms, or by two pairs of gauges making a complete bridge. This arrangement is indicated in Fig. 3.16.

(*D*) *p- and n-type Pairs.* Similar results can be obtained with two gauges mounted side-by-side (i.e. both in tension or compression), if their two characteristics are well matched (Fig. 3.17). The compensation is, however, not perfect since n-type silicon gauges are more non-linear than their p-type counterparts (see Fig. 3.6).

(*E*) *Strain Bias.*   Fig. 3.6 shows that linearity of *p*-type silicon gauges improves with increasing tension, and that of *n*-type gauges with increasing compression. Therefore, if the two matched gauges of the opposite kind are mounted with the appropriate strain biasses, non-linearity in the working strain range is reduced.

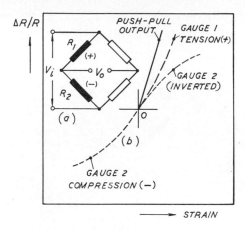

Fig. 3.16 Linearity compensation with push–pull gauges, schematic

3.3.3   *Compensation of Temperature Errors*

Temperature changes in semiconductor strain gauges have two distinct effects: *zero shift* (i.e. apparent strain) and *gauge factor variation.*

(*A*) *Zero Shift.*   With well-matched push–pull gauges, or gauge pairs, zero shift due to temperature change is effectively reduced (see section 3.3.2*C*). In single-gauge installations an inactive dummy gauge of identical temperature characteristic may be substituted, if it operates under similar thermal conditions of heat conduction and dissipation.

The temperature self-compensation of single *n*-type silicon gauges has been discussed in section 3.2.3*C*; another effective method of reducing apparent strain due to temperature changes employs *p*- and *n*-type gauges mounted side-by-side on the test structure, but connected to adjacent arms of the bridge circuit. In *p*-type silicon both the gauge factor and its temperature coefficient are positive, while

n-type silicon has a negative gauge factor and a positive temperature coefficient of gauge factor. Temperature compensation occurs for (section 2.2.2C)

$$s_p - s_n = (|k_p| - |k_n|)(a_s - a_g), \qquad (3.26)$$

where s_p and s_n are the slopes of the $\Delta R/R$ versus temperature curves of p- and n-type silicon respectively, k_p and k_n the respective gauge factors, and a_s and a_g the coefficients of thermal expansion of the test

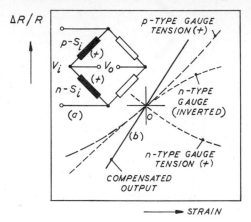

Fig. 3.17 Linearity compensation with p- and n-type silicon gauges mounted side-by-side, schematic

structure (Table 2.4) and of the silicon gauge ($\approx 2.5 \times 10^{-6}$ per degree C). Since s_p and s_n depend on the amount of doping (resistivity) of these materials, temperature compensation is feasible within limits. Further trimming by inserting small lengths of wire with a high temperature coefficient of resistance into the appropriate bridge arm(s) may reduce the apparent strain level to less than 1% of full-scale strain per 100°C over the operational temperature range.

(*B*) *Gauge Factor Variation.* The temperature coefficient of gauge factor of semiconductor strain gauges is negative (Fig. 3.9). A large part of this loss in sensitivity at elevated temperatures, however, is due to the positive temperature coefficient of resistivity (increase of gauge resistance; see section 3.2.3B). Obviously, if the gauge current could be kept constant this loss contribution would be eliminated. Fig. 3.18 shows typical temperature curves for gauge factor

$k = \Delta R/Re$ and for $k' = \Delta R/e$ (i.e. $R =$ constant). The improvement at constant-current operation is apparent.

Constant-current operation can be obtained either by using a

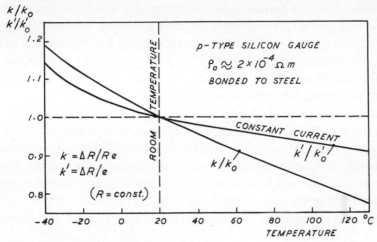

Fig. 3.18 Variation with temperature of gauge factor k and sensitivity k' with respect to their room-temperature values k_0 and k_0', of p-type silicon gauge bonded to steel

constant-current bridge supply, or by artifices in the circuit which produce constant current in the gauges in spite of a constant-voltage bridge supply. In the latter case one (wasteful) method consists of

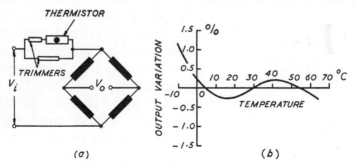

Fig. 3.19 Sensitivity compensation

(a) Thermistor circuit   (b) Bridge output versus temperature

connecting a high resistance in series with the gauge—the high-resistance arms discussed in section 3.3.1 are basically such a device—but another more elegant technique employs temperature-sensitive series resistors. Fig. 3.19a shows a four-arm strain gauge bridge circuit with a thermistor, complete with its trimming resistors, connected in series with the bridge supply. The voltage across the bridge increases as the thermistor resistance falls with rising temperature. The component values of thermistor and trimmers must be chosen such that the increase in bridge output produced by the higher voltage across the bridge compensates for the loss in gauge factor at higher temperatures. Fig. 3.19*b* illustrates the degree of compensation attainable with this method. Thermistor and gauges must, of course, be at the same temperature.

As an alternative to the thermistor, the use of a constant resistor in series with the semiconductor bridge has been suggested. Then, if the gauges have large positive temperature coefficients of resistance, the bridge resistance will rise at increasing temperature and the higher voltage across it will balance the loss in gauge factor. In this method the constant series resistor need not be at the same temperature as the gauges and can therefore be located away from the test structure.

3.3.4   *Zero Adjustment*

It is seen from the above that strain measuring installations with semiconductor gauges derive their linear over-all calibration from a delicate balance of individually non-linear gauge and circuit characteristics. Therefore, if one wishes to 'zero' such a circuit, for instance in order to eliminate the output from an irrelevant preload, conventional methods of bridge adjustment are not suitable, since they would upset the precarious linearity conditions of the bridge. Fig. 3.20 shows an example of zeroing without interfering with the strain gauge proper.

Otherwise, instrumentation for use with semiconductor strain gauges is basically identical with that of wire and foil gauges; at present d.c. operation is perhaps still predominant, but a.c. operation, like that of Fig. 3.20, is also in extensive use.

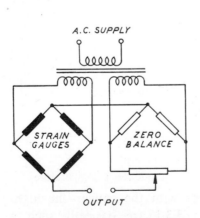

Fig. 3.20 A.C. circuit for independent zero balancing of semiconductor strain gauge bridge

3.4   Comparison Between Semiconductor and Wire Strain Gauges

When discussing in section 1.7.1 the underlying principles of resistance strain gauges we asked the question whether, in search of a strain gauge more sensitive than wire and foil gauges, the modern semiconductor gauge would satisfy the stringent requirements as an accurate and reliable measuring instrument. Now, at the end of our brief excursion into the fascinating field of semiconductors generally, and of silicon strain gauges in particular, our answer should be—yes, with reservations.

There can be no doubt about the much higher sensitivity to strain of the semiconductor gauges; this is their main—and as some critics maintain, only—advantage. For a convenient comparison of the relevant characteristics, Table 3.3 lists the major mechanical and electrical properties of two representative samples: a typical Constantan wire gauge and a general-purpose p-type silicon semiconductor gauge with a room-temperature resistivity of 2×10^{-4} ohm m. The reader will appreciate that the figures quoted in Table 3.3 are average values and must not be taken too literally; nor do they represent any particular commercial product.

As to the mechanical properties, both the breaking strength and the elastic strain range of the silicon filament are higher than those of the Constantan wire, but—as the electrical section of Table 3.3 shows—the useful linear strain range of the uncompensated silicon gauge is only $\pm 0.5 \times 10^{-3}$ m/m. (The figures in brackets apply to single gauges with less severe linearity specifications.) On the other hand, the useful linear range of the wire gauge ($\pm 10^{-3}$ m/m) is set by the mechanical imperfections of the wire, such as plastic flow and hysteresis; linearity of the Constantan gauge is actually maintained up to 50×10^{-3} m/m, and beyond, if these detrimental effects can be disregarded, for instance in dynamic strain measurements.

Apart from non-linearity with respect to strain the vastly larger temperature coefficient of gauge factor in constant-voltage as well as in constant-current operation would make the uncompensated general-purpose silicon gauge a poor competitor of the wire gauge, if reliable compensation techniques were not available. Incidentally, the ratio of the temperature coefficients of resistivity of wire and

TABLE 3.3 Comparison of the Major Properties of Wire Resistance (Constantan) and Semiconductor (*p*-silicon) Strain Gauges at Room Temperatures

	UNITS	WIRE GAUGE	SEMICONDUCTOR GAUGE
(*A*) *Mechanical properties*			
Filament material	—	Constantan	*p*-silicon
Young's modulus	10^{10} N/m^2	16	19
Poisson's ratio	—	0·33	0·18
Max. breaking strength	10^8 N/m^2	4·6	20
Min. radius of curvature	10^{-3} m	0·5	3
Max. strain	10^{-3} m/m	50	4
Max. elastic strain	10^{-3} m/m	1	4
Min. filament cross-section	10^{-10} m^2	1	2
Min. gauge length	10^{-3} m	2	2
Fatigue life at $e = \pm 10^{-3}$	cycles	$>10^7$	$>10^7$
(*B*) *Electrical properties*			
Gauge factor	—	2	120
Useful linear range (uncompensated)	10^{-3} m/m	± 1	± 0.5
Temperature coefficient of gauge factor (uncompensated; constant-voltage operation)	10^{-6}/°C	(50)	(−0·5 to +3)
Temperature coefficient of gauge factor (uncompensated; constant-current operation)	10^{-6}/°C	<1	−3500
Useful temperature range (acceptable temperature stability)	°C	−80 to +250	−40 to +100
Operational temperature range (stable gauge bonding)	°C	−80 to +250	−80 to +250
Resistivity	10^{-6} Ω m	0·45	200
Temperature coefficient of resistivity	10^{-4}/°C	± 0.2	+10
Apparent strain on aluminium (uncompensated)	10^{-3}/°C	0·015	2·6
Gauge resistance	Ω	10^2 to 10^3	10^2 to 10^4
Normal gauge current (on metals)	10^{-3} A	20	20
(*C*) *Miscellaneous*			
Ruggedness in handling	—	good	fair
Cost per gauge	shilling	5 to 10	60 to 120

silicon gauges about equals the ratio of their gauge factors; therefore, in order to maintain an edge on the wire gauge in this respect, the silicon gauge would depend on compensation artifices, anyway. The same applies to the higher values of apparent strain in silicon gauges at variable temperatures.

From the performance figures of Table 3.3, and from our more detailed discussion earlier in this chapter, it is quite obvious that the superiority—or even compatibility—of the semiconductor strain gauge in practical strain gauging depends all along on sophisticated and often rather precarious compensation techniques. Our earlier reservation on its usefulness should therefore be stated thus: If—and only if—the potential user of semiconductor strain gauges fully appreciates their peculiarities, and is prepared to take the trouble of putting into effect, and maintaining, the necessary compensation artifices, can he be sure of obtaining meaningful and accurate results from his strain measurements.

Nevertheless, in all cases where high sensitivity is a real necessity, the semiconductor strain gauge—in spite of its higher cost—is an economical and most welcome solution to many measuring problems which are not accessible to conventional strain gauges. The beginner in the art of strain gauging, however, is well advised to build his expertise in this field first on a solid foundation of wire and foil gauging techniques before he ventures into semiconductors.

4 Evaluation of Strain Measurements

In this chapter there are, in principle, two extreme paths open to the writer; he can either settle down to a comprehensive treatment of the physics of solid matter under stress, supported by a full display of the classical theory of elasticity of idealised, three-dimensional structures, or just show how to obtain the principal stresses from multiple-gauge strain measurements in a two-dimensional stress field.

Although only the first approach would fully satisfy the conscientious reader—and the writer—it would fill a book larger than the present volume. The second path, when taken too narrowly, would lead merely to manipulating obscure formulae. As matters are, we must leave the fundamentals of solid state physics and theory of elasticity to the reader's conscience and curiosity (there is a short bibliography at the end of the book) and try to answer here the practical question: What direct information can we get from our strain measurements?

4.1 Stress and Strain

4.1.1 *Properties of Engineering Materials*

Since the primary purpose of strain gauging is the safety of loaded structures, we would expect that the theory of fracture would lead us to the most significant stress parameters. There is, in fact, more than one theory of fracture; in brittle materials it is the maximum (tensile) stress which usually is held responsible for ultimate failure (St. Venant, Lamé), while for ductile materials according to one view the maximum shear stresses (Guest), and according to another the maximum strain energy (Girtler, Haigh) are considered of greater importance. More recent theories are concerned with the occurrence and propagation of microscopic imperfections in and around the crystals of stressed materials (grain boundaries, slip planes, dislocations, etc.). However, these microscopic effects are not directly accessible to strain gauging.

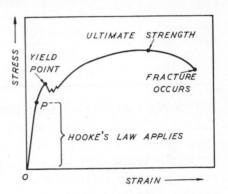

Fig. 4.1 Stress/strain relationship in tensile test of mild steel, schematic

Indeed, the strength of a perfect crystal, computed from the atomic binding forces in the lattice, should be several orders higher than that known for the same polycrystalline engineering material, though very thin filaments (*whiskers*) of some materials with perfectly clean and smooth surfaces have been found to approach the theoretical values. Hence the recent trend to the use of bundles of thin filaments, e.g. glass or carbon fibres, embedded in a matrix of a suitable plastic.

The classical tensile test reveals another aspect of the imperfection of ordinary engineering materials. Fig. 4.1 shows schematically the well known stress/strain curve of soft mild steel. The initial part is distorted; the slope should be much steeper, since it represents a strain range of only about 0·1%, while fracture occurs at well above 30% strain. The fine structure of the initial part would also show that above a point P the curve deviates distinctly from a straight line. This point is the limit of proportionality, or elasticity,* up to which Hooke's law of linear relation between stress and strain applies. Rough values of the limit of elasticity of some materials are given in Table 4.1.

* The limit of perfect elasticity may be slightly lower than that of proportionality.

Further, if a structure was previously stressed beyond the elastic limit, and is then released of its load, the strain does not disappear completely and a residual (plastic) strain will remain (hysteresis). Also, in this plastic region of stress the strain may increase with time, although the load remains substantially constant (creep).

TABLE 4.1   Limits of Elasticity

	SPRING STEEL	MILD STEEL	BRASS
Stress (10^8 N/m^2)	>5 (annealed) >7·5 (hardened)	2–5	0·6 (cast)

Together with the elongation there is also a lateral contraction of the test rod. In the elastic region the ratio of lateral to longitudinal strain (Poisson's ratio) is a constant which has values between zero for ideally brittle materials with no lateral contraction, and 0·5 for perfectly plastic deformation, where there can be no change in volume. Practical values for most metals are near 0·3.

Other important aspects of the behaviour of engineering materials are related to recurring stress cycles (internal damping and fatigue), to stress concentrations near holes and notches (or just roughly machined or damaged surfaces), and to transient impact loading; they can only be mentioned here. Generally, heat treatment of metals—particularly of steel—and of some plastics affects greatly the over-all, or local, elastic properties, and so does cold working.

From the foregoing it is apparent that the information we can expect from strain gauge measurements will normally be restricted to the range of Hooke's law, since it is unlikely that manageable relations between strains and stresses can be established in stress regions where non-linearity, hysteresis and creep prevail.* Although a direct answer to the question of ultimate breaking strength of a

---

* Note that this limitation stems from the difficulty of evaluating stress distributions from strain measurements in the plastic region. Although semiconductor strain gauges can stand strains only up to 0·4%, most wire and foil gauges can indicate direct strains up to 2 or 5%, depending on gauge type, and so-called *post-yield* gauges go up to 10%, i.e. near the ultimate strain of many materials, except the most ductile. But their stress/strain 'calibration' curve would resemble Fig. 4.1, and since Hooke's law does not apply, the law of superposition does not hold. (Post-yield strain gauges can be used only once.)

particular structure can not, therefore, be expected, comprehensive information on the strain and stress distribution in the elastic region, i.e. magnitudes and directions of the maximum normal and shear strains and stresses, will be of great assistance in assessing the load-carrying capacity and optimum load distribution of a structure; it will also help in arriving at a suitable safety factor.

After these cautionary remarks on the wider issues of strain evaluation we shall now move on to the firmer grounds of numerical stress and strain analysis of well-behaved materials.

4.1.2 *The Elastic Constants*

The theory of elasticity deals with solid bodies; in contrast to liquids and gases solid materials resist deformation. A small volume element inside such a deformed body experiences on its boundaries with adjacent volume elements forces and moments, but with decreasing size the couples vanish faster than the forces, since their arms vanish also. An elementary surface of a volume element can therefore transmit only forces, and their normal and tangential components, when related to an elementary surface area, are known as normal stresses σ (N/m^2) and shear stresses τ (N/m^2). At a particular point in the stressed body there are thus three normal stresses, corresponding to the three spatial axes x, y, z, and since shear is operating in a plane, also six shear stresses; i.e. a total of nine stress components.

In the most general case each of these nine stress components could be affected by nine similar deformation or strain components, giving a total of $9 \times 9 = 81$ factors of proportionality between stress and strain. At closer inspection, however, this number can be reduced appreciably. For reasons of force equilibrium related shear stresses are equal, and some components are not relevant since they indicate only rotation, not strain. Considerations of strain energy reduces the number further, though in a totally anisotropic medium (i.e. a material which has different elastic properties in different directions) there are still 21 proportionality factors left.

An isotropic material has no preferred directions; complete interchangeability of axes, then, reduces the number of factors to three, and within the validity range of Hooke's law of direct proportionality between stress and strain the relevant elastic constants become the following:

Modulus of elasticity or Young's modulus	$E = \sigma/e$ (N/m²)	(4.1a)
Modulus of rigidity	$G = \tau/\gamma$ (N/m²)	(4.1b)
Poisson's ratio	ν	(4.1c)

where e is the direct or normal strain, γ the shear strain and ν (<1) the ratio of lateral contraction to longitudinal elongation. These three elastic constants are valid for volume elements of isotropic materials; for their application in the stress analysis of structures of finite size the material must also be homogeneous.

The three material constants E, G and ν are related thus:

$$E = 2G(1 + \nu) \tag{4.2a}$$

$$G = \frac{E}{2(1 + \nu)} \tag{4.2b}$$

$$\nu = \frac{E}{2G} - 1 \tag{4.2c}$$

and the so-called *bulk modulus* (volumetric stiffness) is

$$K = \frac{E}{3(1 - 2\nu)}. \tag{4.2d}$$

Table 4.2 lists approximate values for Young's modulus E and Poisson's ratio ν, of a number of common, and some not-so-common,

TABLE 4.2   Elastic Constants of Some Structural Materials, near Room Temperature

MATERIALS	YOUNG'S MODULUS E (N/m²) (to be multiplied by 10^{10})	POISSON'S RATIO ν
Aluminium	7·0	0·34
Belt, leather	(2·5–4) × 10^{-3}	—
Brass	10	0·35
Brick	1–1·5	—
Concrete	2·5–3·5	—
Copper	11–13	0·34
Duralumin	7·1	0·34
Glass	5–7	0·2–0·3

TABLE 4.2—*Continued*

MATERIALS	YOUNG'S MODULUS $E(N/m^2)$ (to be multiplied by 10^{10})	POISSON'S RATIO v
Iron		
wrought	19–20	0·29
cast	10–13	0·2–0·3
Marble	3–4	—
Nickel	20·4	0·28
Phosphor bronze	12	0·38
Plastics		
thermo-plastic	0·15–0·3	—
thermo-setting	0·3–1·2	—
Rubber, soft	$(1·5–5) \times 10^{-4}$	0·45–0·5
Steel	21	0·29
Stone, natural	1–3	—
Titanium	11·6	0·32
Tungsten	30–35	—
Wood		
‖ grain	0·5–1·2	—
⊥ grain	0·05–0·2	—
Zinc	8·7	0·21

structural materials. (The modulus of rigidity G and the bulk modulus K can be computed from these according to equations 4.2b and d, respectively.) Since the elastic properties of most materials deteriorate at higher temperatures the values of Young's modulus in Table 4.2 should be multiplied by a factor $1 + n\Delta\theta$, where $\Delta\theta$ (°C) is the temperature increase above room temperature, and n the (negative) temperature coefficient of E. Table 4.3 lists values of n for a few materials, though at small temperature variations these corrections can usually be neglected in view of the wide tolerances of Table 4.2.

TABLE 4.3   Temperature Coefficients of Young's Modulus (10^4 per degree C) of Some Materials

ALUMINIUM	BRASS	COPPER	IRON	STEEL
−4·8	−3·7	−3·0	−2·3	−2·4

4.1.3   *Two-dimensional Stress Analysis*

It is fortunate that the most critical regions of a structure under stress and strain occur almost invariably on its surface and are thus

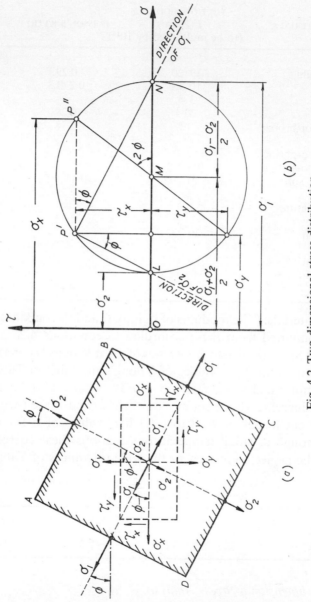

Fig. 4.2 Two-dimensional stress distribution
(a) Stress pattern at arbitrary angle ϕ
(b) Mohr's stress circle

accessible to strain measurements. Our practical interest, therefore, lies with two-dimensional strain and stress distributions, as the third stress component normal to the surface vanishes near the surface. Normally, we can also assume that the test structure is isotropic, homogeneous and elastic, i.e. Hooke's law holds. Strains and stresses can then be superimposed and E, G and ν are constants.

Consider Fig. 4.2a. The surface area $ABCD$ is subjected to the orthogonal principal stresses σ_1 and σ_2 (where $\sigma_1 > \sigma_2$) and we wish to find the normal and shear stresses that occur in arbitrary directions ϕ and $\phi + \pi/2$, relative to the directions of σ_1 and σ_2. With a co-ordinate system x, y, fixed to the ϕ-direction, as shown in Fig. 4.2a, the so-called *Mohr's stress circle* can be constructed according to Fig. 4.2b. The point P' has been obtained by drawing two parallels to the σ_1- and σ_2-directions through L and N, respectively, the intersections of the σ-axis with a circle of radius $(\sigma_1 - \sigma_2)/2$ about a centre M which is displaced from the τ-axis by a distance $(\sigma_1 + \sigma_2)/2$. The point P'' is the mirror image of P' about the vertical through M.

The normal and shear stresses related to the ϕ-direction can now be read from Fig. 4.2b:

$$\sigma_\phi = \sigma_x = \tfrac{1}{2}\{(\sigma_1 + \sigma_2) + (\sigma_1 - \sigma_2)\cos 2\phi\} \qquad (4.3a)$$

$$\sigma_{\phi + \pi/2} = \sigma_y = \tfrac{1}{2}\{(\sigma_1 + \sigma_2) - (\sigma_1 - \sigma_2)\cos 2\phi\} \qquad (4.3b)$$

$$\tau^{\phi,\phi+\pi/2} = \tau_{x,y} = \pm\ \tfrac{1}{2}(\sigma_1 - \sigma_2)\sin 2\phi. \qquad (4.3c)$$

In a similar fashion a Mohr's circle could also be drawn for the strain distributions. From this we would obtain:

$$e_\phi = \tfrac{1}{2}\{(e_1 + e_2) + (e_1 - e_2)\cos 2\phi\} \qquad (4.4a)$$

$$e_{\phi + \pi/2} = \tfrac{1}{2}\{(e_1 + e_2) - (e_1 - e_2)\cos 2\phi\} \qquad (4.4b)$$

$$\gamma_{\phi,\phi+\pi/2} = \pm(e_1 - e_2)\sin 2\phi. \qquad (4.4c)$$

Note the missing factor $\tfrac{1}{2}$ in equation 4.4c.

4.1.4   *Stress and Strain Distribution in a Long Rod under Tension*

As an illustration we shall now analyse in detail the simple, though important case of a long rod under longitudinal stress σ_1 (see section 1.1). Since here $\sigma_2 = 0$, this is known as uniaxial stress distribution, but because of lateral contraction according to $e_2 = -ve_1$, the strain distribution is, of course, distinctly two-dimensional.

Consider a long rod of duralumin, 1·5 cm wide and 0·5 cm thick, which is loaded in tension by a force of 2000 newton. A special inductance strain gauge which measured longitudinal and shear strain separately was attached to the flat surface of the rod at different angles ϕ to the rod axis. The experimental strain values are plotted in the polar diagram of Fig. 4.3a over the range $0 < \phi < \pi/2$. The accurate value of Poisson's ratio e_2/e_1 was 0·337. From equation 4.4a the angular distribution of the normal strain e should be

$$e_\phi = \frac{e_1}{2}\{(1 - v) + (1 + v) \cos 2\phi\} \tag{4.5}$$

and from equation 4.4c the shear strain distribution

$$\gamma_\phi = e_1(1 + v) \sin 2\phi. \tag{4.6}$$

Computed values of e_ϕ and $\gamma_\phi/2$ * as functions of the angle ϕ have also been plotted in Fig. 4.3a as solid and dotted lines, respectively. The strain scale is fixed by the value of e_1; with the foregoing equations we have for the duralumin rod under tension:

Load	$F = 2000$ N
Cross-section	$a = 75 \times 10^{-6}$ m²
Young's modulus	$E = 7\cdot1 \times 10^{10}$ N/m²
Poisson's ratio	$v = 0\cdot337$
Principal } stresses ∫	$\sigma_1 = F/a = 26\cdot7 \times 10^6$ N/m² $\sigma_2 = 0$
Max. shear stress	$\tau_{max} = \frac{1}{2}(\sigma_1 - \sigma_2) = \frac{1}{2}\sigma_1 = 13\cdot35 \times 10^6$ N/m²
Principal } strains ∫	$e_1 = \sigma_1/E = 3\cdot76 \times 10^{-4}$ m/m $e_2 = -ve_1 = -1\cdot27 \times 10^{-4}$ m/m
Max. shear strain	$\gamma_{max} = e_1(1 + v) = 5\cdot02 \times 10^{-4}$ m/m.

The complete two-dimensional strain pattern for $0 < \phi < 2\pi$ can be obtained by reflecting Fig. 4.3a in the vertical and horizontal axes of symmetry; it consists of two major ($\pm e_1$) and two minor ($\pm e_2$)

---

* According to equations 4.3c and 4.4c, τ_ϕ is analogous to $\gamma_\phi/2$, not to γ_ϕ.

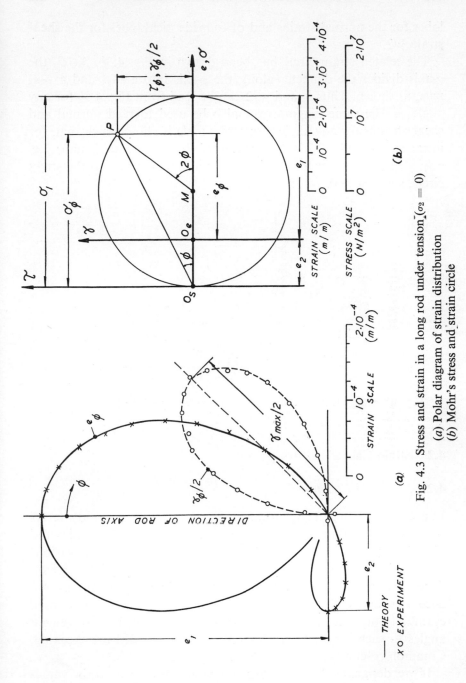

Fig. 4.3 Stress and strain in a long rod under tension ($\sigma_2 = 0$)

(a) Polar diagram of strain distribution
(b) Mohr's stress and strain circle

lobes for the normal strains and of four identical lobes for the shear strain $\gamma/2$.

The related strain circle has been drawn in Fig. 4.3b. At O_e the γ-axis divides the diameter along the e-axis into a $+e_1$ and a $-e_2$ part, as shown. Thus e_ϕ and $\gamma_\phi/2$ can be read from Fig. 4.3b for any angle ϕ. The same diagram can also be used to read normal and shear stresses for any angle, if a stress scale is chosen such that, for instance, τ_ϕ and $\gamma_\phi/2$ are represented by the same length; i.e. $\tau_\phi/\gamma_\phi = G$. Note that the τ-axis is here a tangent at O_s to the stress circle, since $\sigma_2 = 0$.

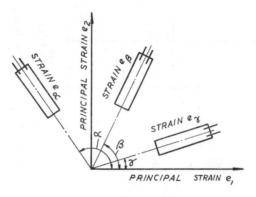

Fig. 4.4 Three-element rosette, general (angles anticlockwise relative to e_1; $e_1 > e_2$)

4.2　Strain Gauge Rosettes

4.2.1　*Strain Distribution*

In practical strain gauging, however, the principal strains and stresses are unknown and the problem, then, is to find their magnitudes and directions from a number of strain measurements taken at various angles. Since equation 4.4 has three unknowns, e_1, e_2 and ϕ, three independent strain measurements in three different directions are necessary and sufficient. Strain gauge rosettes, therefore, consist essentially of three (identical) strain gauges arranged at convenient angles to each other; a fourth gauge may be added for checking. Common rosette types will be discussed in section 4.2.3.

If we designate the three experimentally obtained strain values

e_α, e_β, e_γ, taken at angles α, β, γ, * respectively (Fig. 4.4), then we may rewrite equation 4.4a as

$$e_\phi = A + B \cos 2\phi \qquad (4.7)$$

where ϕ assumes the values α, β and γ, and

$$A = \tfrac{1}{2}(e_1 + e_2) \qquad \text{(abscissa of centre} \qquad (4.8a)$$
$$\text{of strain circle)}$$

$$B = \tfrac{1}{2}(e_1 - e_2) \qquad \text{(radius of strain circle),} \quad (4.8b)$$

or the principal strains ($e_1 < e_2$) are

$$e_1 = A + B \qquad (4.9a)$$
$$e_2 = A - B \qquad (4.9b)$$

and the maximum shear strain is

$$\gamma_{max} = e_1 - e_2 = 2B \qquad (4.9c)$$

with the convention that positive strain represents elongation. The strain field, then, is completely determined if the values of A and B and one angle, say α, are known for a particular rosette configuration.

4.2.2 *Stress Distribution*

Likewise, the stress distribution, i.e. the magnitudes and directions of the principal stresses σ_1 and σ_2 (where $\sigma_1 > \sigma_2$) can be derived from the principal strains:

$$\sigma_1 = \frac{E}{1 - \nu^2}(e_1 + \nu e_2) \qquad (4.10a)$$

$$\sigma_2 = \frac{E}{1 - \nu^2}(e_2 + \nu e_1) \qquad (4.10b)$$

where E (N/m^2) is the Young's modulus and ν the Poisson's ratio of the test material. For ease of analysis we substitute here:

$$\sigma_1 = C + D \qquad (4.11a)$$
$$\sigma_2 = C - D \qquad (4.11b)$$

and for the maximum shear stress

$$\tau_{max} = \tfrac{1}{2}(\sigma_1 - \sigma_2) = D \qquad (4.11c)$$

* Not to be confused with shear strain.

where

$$C = AE/(1 - \nu) \quad \text{(abscissa of centre} \qquad (4.12a)$$
$$\text{of stress circle)}$$

$$D = BE/(1 + \nu) \quad \text{(radius of stress circle).} \quad (4.12b)$$

The complete stress field is thus determined; the values of A and B (equation 4.8) are, again, related to a particular rosette configuration, while the directions of the principal stresses are identical with those of the principal strains.

In the section to follow we shall discuss common rosette types and give analytical expressions for A, B and α.

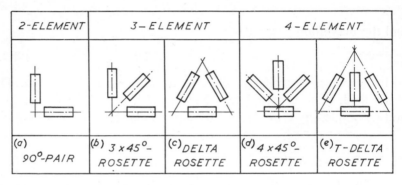

Fig. 4.5 Common rosette types

4.2.3 *Rosette Types*

Fig. 4.5 shows the most common types of strain gauge rosettes.* The 90°-pair (*a*) for the measurement of shear or torque is strictly not a rosette gauge, since it does not permit the complete measurement of a two-dimensional strain distribution, unless the directions of the principal strains have been established accurately by other means (e.g. the brittle lacquer method) and the two legs of the 90°-pair are mounted exactly along these lines. For the measurement of shear and torque the gauge is applied as shown in Fig. 2.10 of Chapter 2.

In some cases the orientation of the stress field may, however, be

---

* Fig. 4.5 shows the 'open' gauge arrangements; there are also versions of these types with the gauges superimposed. A selection of a few commercial gauge types is included in Table 2.3 of Chapter 2.

roughly known. Then the $3 \times 45°$-rosette of Fig. 4.5b gives particularly accurate results, if its two orthogonal gauges are pointing approximately in the directions of the principal strains. For the subsequent analytical evaluation of magnitude and direction of principal strains and stresses Fig. 4.6a gives the appropriate values of A and B

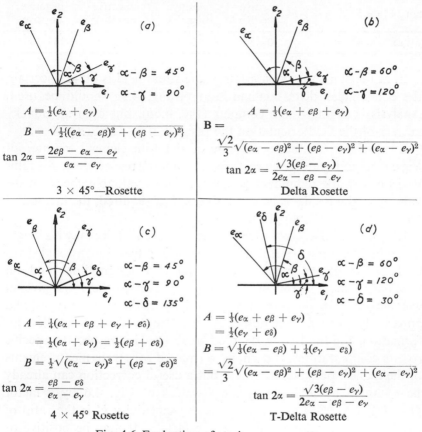

Fig. 4.6 Evaluation of strain gauge rosettes

for substitution into equations 4.9, 4.11 and 4.12. It also gives an expression for 2α, but since the angle α is not uniquely defined by the magnitude of $\tan 2\alpha$, its valid range must be decided upon by reference to Table 4.4.

The principal strains and stresses and their angular orientation α with respect to the gauge can thus be computed from the measured strains e_α, e_β, e_γ (see example in next section) and the complete two-dimensional stress and strain field is determined. A small correction for errors due to transverse sensitivity of the gauges will be discussed presently.

TABLE 4.4   Valid Ranges of α for Numerical Values of tan $2\alpha = a/b$

tan $2\alpha = a/b$	a	positive	positive	negative	negative
	b	positive	negative	negative	positive
VALID RANGE OF α		0–45°	45–90°	90–135°	135–180°

If, at the start, the orientation of the stress field is quite uncertain the equiangular delta configuration of Fig. 4.5c should be used. Analysis is slightly more complex (Fig. 4.6b), but even at unlucky guesses of the field orientation the result will be satisfactory.

Expressions for the evaluation of the four-element rosettes of Figs. 4.5d and e are given in Figs. 4.6c and d, respectively. By comparison with the redundant gauge readings a valuable check on the validity of the results is here possible and, if required, the method of least squares can be applied.

It is obvious that errors due to transverse sensitivity may no longer be negligible, if high lateral stresses occur in a two-dimensional stress field. Some gauge manufacturers quote a longitudinal and an 'auxiliary' gauge factor on their gauge packets; others just give an average value for the transverse sensitivity of their gauge types, and apparently some do not bother at all. The need for the fullest information, followed by a detailed analysis with respect to specific rosette configurations, is perhaps warrented for strain measurements of the highest possible accuracy, but a useful correction can already be obtained by multiplying the B-values of Fig. 4.6 by a factor $(1 + k')/(1 - k')$, where the transverse sensitivity k' is the ratio of the lateral to the longitudinal gauge factors. It may be positive or negative, depending on gauge construction, but should not be greater than a couple of per cent at the most.

4.2.4   *Example of Numerical Evaluation of Rosette Measurements*

In order to illustrate in practice the procedure for computing the stress distribution from given rosette measurements we shall assume that the orientation of the field is unknown, so that a delta-rosette gauge, as in Fig. 4.5c, is used.

Let us consider the following data, referring to a test structure of duralumin:

Young's modulus	$E = 7 \cdot 1 \times 10^{10}$ N/m²
Poisson's ratio	$v = 0 \cdot 34$
Gauge factor	$k = 2 \cdot 0$
Transverse sensitivity ratio	$k' = +0 \cdot 012$.

Measured specific resistance changes:

$$(\Delta R/R)_\alpha = +10 \times 10^{-4} \text{ ohm/ohm}$$
$$(\Delta R/R)_\beta = +8 \times 10^{-4} \text{ ohm/ohm}$$
$$(\Delta R/R)_\gamma = +4 \times 10^{-4} \text{ ohm/ohm}$$

and since $e = (\Delta R/R)/k$, the corresponding strain values are

$$e_\alpha = +5 \times 10^{-4} \text{ m/m}$$
$$e_\beta = +4 \times 10^{-4} \text{ m/m}$$
$$e_\gamma = +2 \times 10^{-4} \text{ m/m}$$

i.e. well within the validity of Hooke's law. Now, from Fig. 4.6b:

$$A = \tfrac{1}{3}(e_\alpha + e_\beta + e_\gamma) = \tfrac{1}{3}(5 + 4 + 2) \times 10^{-4} = 3 \cdot 67 \times 10^{-4} \text{ m/m}$$

$$B = \frac{\sqrt{2}}{3}\{(e_\alpha - e_\beta)^2 + (e_\beta - e_\gamma)^2 + (e_\alpha - e_\gamma)^2\}^{\frac{1}{2}}$$

$$= \frac{\sqrt{2}}{3}\{(1 + 4 + 9) \times 10^{-8}\}^{\frac{1}{2}} = 1 \cdot 77 \times 10^{-4} \text{ m/m}$$

or, when the correction for transverse sensitivity is applied to B,

$$1 \cdot 77 \times 10^{-4}(1 + k')/(1 - k') = 1 \cdot 77 \times 10^{-4} \times 1 \cdot 012/0 \cdot 988$$
$$= 1 \cdot 81 \times 10^{-4} \text{ m/m}.$$

The orientation of the strain and stress field is also obtained from Fig. 4.6b:

$$\tan 2\alpha = \frac{\sqrt{3}(e_\beta - e_\gamma)}{2e_\alpha - e_\beta - e_\gamma} = \frac{\sqrt{3}(4 - 2)}{10 - 4 - 2} = 0 \cdot 867.$$

Since both numerator and denominator are positive the α-range according to Table 4.4 is $0°$–$45°$; i.e.

$$2\alpha = 40° \, 55', \qquad \alpha = 20° \, 28'.$$

E

Now, the principal strains are (equation 4.9)

$$e_1 = A + B = (3\cdot67 + 1\cdot81) \times 10^{-4} = 5\cdot48 \times 10^{-4} \text{ m/m}$$
$$e_2 = A - B = (3\cdot67 - 1\cdot81) \times 10^{-4} = 1\cdot86 \times 10^{-4} \text{ m/m}$$

and the maximum shear strain is

$$\gamma_{max} = 2B = 2 \times 1\cdot81 \times 10^{-4} = 3\cdot62 \times 10^{-4} \text{ m/m}.$$

The stress distribution can now be obtained from equations 4.11 and 4.12;

$$C = \frac{AE}{1 - \nu} = \frac{3\cdot67 \times 10^{-4} \times 7\cdot1 \times 10^{10}}{1 - 0\cdot34} = 39\cdot5 \times 10^6 \text{ N/m}^2$$

$$D = \frac{BE}{1 + \nu} = \frac{1\cdot81 \times 10^{-4} \times 7\cdot1 \times 10^{10}}{1 + 0\cdot34} = 9\cdot6 \times 10^6 \text{ N/m}^2.$$

From this the principal stresses are

$$\sigma_1 = C + D = (39\cdot5 + 9\cdot6) \times 10^6 = 49\cdot1 \times 10^6 \text{ N/m}^2$$
$$\sigma_2 = C - D = (39\cdot5 - 9\cdot6) \times 10^6 = 29\cdot9 \times 10^6 \text{ N/m}^2$$

and the maximum shear stress is

$$\tau_{max} = D = 9\cdot6 \times 10^6 \text{ N/m}^2.$$

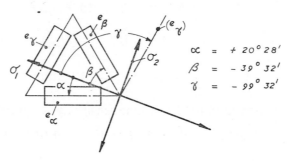

Fig. 4.7 Direction of principal stresses relative to delta-rosette gauge
(see text)

In conclusion, Fig. 4.7 shows the relative magnitudes of the principal stresses σ_1 and σ_2, and their directions with respect to the position of the delta-rosette gauge. The lines are drawn through a corner of the gauge pattern for convenience only; the stress and strain field must be assumed uniform over the whole gauge area, which therefore determines the spatial resolution of the gauge.

It should also be mentioned here that, besides the analytical method of rosette evaluation explained above, alternative methods of solution by nomographs, charts and special slide rules have been developed, and solutions by vector methods and by graphical technique, based on Mohr's circle, are also known from the literature. They are of particular value if a large number of strain measurements must be processed in the shortest possible time.

5 Strain Gauge Transducers

Apart from the measurement for their own sake of local strains and strain distributions in loaded structures, strain gauges are now being used to an increasing extent in the measurement of other physical quantities, for instance force or pressure, which can be reduced to strain in simple stressed components, such as cantilevers and diaphragms.

In our brief survey in this chapter on strain gauge transducers we shall restrict the discussion to variable-resistance strain gauges (wire and semiconductor, bonded and unbonded) employed in the measurement of forces (load, thrust, torque), of absolute and differential pressures, and of acceleration. Also, since the diversities and numbers of strain gauge transducers are even greater than those of strain gauges proper, it will not be possible here to give selective lists of commercially available instruments. In fact, we shall have to limit our discussion to basic principles and typical designs of representative transducers. The reader should then be capable of selecting a suitable configuration for his particular need.

Most wire and semiconductor strain gauge manufacturers in this country and abroad (see sections 2.1.4 and 3.1.4) offer also a range of strain gauge transducers, employing their own *bonded* gauges in one way or another; the major suppliers of *unbonded* strain gauge transducers are:

Bell & Howell, Ltd., Consolidated Electrodynamics Division, Basingstoke, Hants.

Ether Engineering, Ltd., Park Avenue, Bushey, Herts.

Statham Instruments, Inc., Los Angeles 64, Calif., U.S.A.

5.1   Force and Torque Transducers

Although pressure and acceleration transducers are basically also force measuring devices, in this section we shall consider the direct measurement of force (and force couples, i.e. torque) by means of bonded strain gauges, but at the end we shall also add a description of force measuring devices with freely suspended wires under stress which form the sensing elements of the well known *unbonded strain gauge* pressure and acceleration transducers to be discussed in sections 5.2.4 and 5.3.2, respectively.

We shall start with simple dynamometers and load cells for the measurement of unidirectional forces and couples, and then proceed to more complex devices, such as wind-tunnel balances, for the simultaneous measurement of three-dimensional forces and couples. Section 5.1.4 will deal with the principles of gauge selection for transducer application.

5.1.1   *Dynamometers and Load Cells*

Force measuring transducers are commonly known as *dynamometers*. If they are intended for weighing purpose they are referred to as *load cells*. Fig. 5.1 shows a number of basic arrangements for force and torque measurement by means of bonded strain gauges.

The slender tension rod of Fig. 5.1*a* may be used with one or two bonded strain gauges in tension oriented parallel to the rod axis. One or two further gauges arranged normal to the axis will pick up the lateral compressive strain (see section 4.1.4) which is about 30% of the axial strain; but their main purpose is temperature compensation, which could also be achieved by dummy gauges in thermal contact only with the rod.

In spite of its simplicity, however, the rod-type dynamometer is of little use since the generation of reasonable strain levels requires high forces and gauge attachment is inconvenient. Because of the

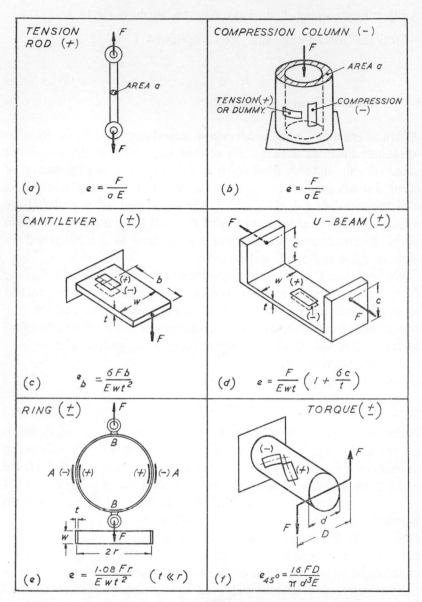

Fig. 5.1 Some basic force and torque transducers with bonded strain gauges, schematic

danger of buckling it is unsuitable for the measurement of compressive forces.

Fig. 5.1*b* shows schematically a hollow column (tube) under compression for the measurement of weight or thrust (load cell), but solid columns have also been used for high loads. Four gauges for complete bridge operation can conveniently be attached to the cylinder surface. They should be arranged around the circumference so that non-uniform stresses in the column, due to non-symmetrical loading, are compensated. The cross-sectional area *a* can be reduced further by longitudinal slits (not shown), in order to increase the local strain under the gauges at given loads.

The design of, and the choice and treatment of materials for, high-class load cells, together with the selection and elaborate technique of gauge attachment of high-stability strain gauges and their temperature compensation, require a wealth of experience and cannot be discussed here in any detail (see section 5.1.4). Likewise, specialised electronic circuitry and read-out equipment has reached a high degree of perfection such that strain gauge type load cells are now comparable with, if not superior to, other kinds of precision weighing equipment.

At lower force levels a more efficient strain generator is required. This can be achieved with bending elements. Fig. 5.1*c* shows a simple cantilever with gauges attached to top and bottom of the lever near its root. Since the maximum strain $e_{max} = 6Fl/Ewt^2$, where l is the length of the lever, occurs at the clamping point, it is not accessible to gauges of finite length; the usable strain e_b may therefore be appreciably smaller, particularly in short cantilevers.

The two gauges in Fig. 5.1*c* operate as a push–pull pair at identical tensile ($+$) and compressive ($-$) strain levels. Two more gauges can be added for improved sensitivity and temperature compensation.

The embarrassment of the non-uniform strain distribution along the axis of the simple cantilever is eliminated in the U-shaped beam of Fig. 5.1*d*. Here the bending moment, and thus the strain, is uniform over the centre part of the U and the gauges can be attached without loss in sensitivity anywhere along the beam. The expression in Fig. 5.1*d* for the strain applies to tensile forces; under compression the force/strain relationship is non-linear, except at negligible deflexions.

Fig. 5.1*e* shows the well known *ring dynamometer*. Elongation of the ring in the direction of pull produces tensile and compressive strains at *A* on the internal and external faces of the flat ring, as shown in the figure. Under compression their polarities are reversed. If the ring thickness *t* is small compared with the radius *r*, positive and negative strains are about equal and can be computed from the formula quoted in Fig. 5.1*e*. With thick rings for the measurement of large forces this does not hold and individual calibration is required. Incidentally, compressive strain occurs also at *B* but, although it is almost twice as high as that at *A*, the stiffening effect of the lugs is rather unpredictable.

5.1.2   *Torque Meters*

The method of measuring torque by way of two strain gauges arranged at 45° with respect to the axis of a shaft is already known from Fig. 2.10. It can be shown that the two principal strains occur at $\pm 45°$ to the direction of the pure shear strain (produced by the torque) and that they are of opposite polarity; their absolute values are identical and equal to the shear strain given in Fig. 5.1*f*. For improved output and stability, and for an effective compensation of thrust and bending stresses possibly present in the shaft, a second pair of gauges can be used on the other side of the shaft. The reader should verify this statement by considering the magnitudes and polarities of the output from four active gauges connected in a complete bridge circuit; this arrangement is also of particular benefit with respect to slip-ring performance (see below).

In the measurement of low-level torque the shaft often becomes too thin for convenient gauge attachment. Thin-walled tubes might be the answer, or a 'squirrel-cage' type torque meter can be designed with four bars of rectangular cross-section machined from the solid shaft and provided with strain gauges bonded at the appropriate locations for complete bridge operation.

An extended application of the torque meter is shown in Fig. 5.2. If the input voltage to the torque meter bridge is V_i, then the output voltage V_o' at torque M is

$$V_o = C_1 V_i M \qquad (5.1)$$

where C_1 is a proportionality factor. Now, if the input voltage to the bridge is made proportional to the engine speed n, the output voltage V_o' is proportional to engine power:

$$V_o' = C_1 C_2 n M \tag{5.2}$$

where C_2 is a calibration factor of the tachometer. Further, integrating V_o' with respect to time yields the energy, or work, delivered by the engine over specific periods of time.

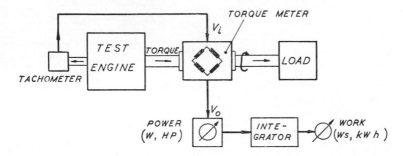

Fig. 5.2 Measurement of torque, power and work of a test engine, schematic

Almost invariably * the torque meter requires the use of slip-rings as vital links between the gauges on the rotating shaft and the stationary read-out equipment. It will be obvious that a gliding contact (brush on ring) produces resistance variations ('noise') and it is therefore essential that the slip-ring contacts are not connected in series with the strain gauges. This can be achieved by having the complete Wheatstone bridge rotating with the shaft; the bridge then, is fed via one pair of brushes and the output is extracted by another pair. In this case the resistance variations caused by the slip-rings do not compete directly with the gauge resistances, and only scale errors, not zero errors, are produced by the slip-rings. Since the spurious resistance variations will be small compared with the diagonal resistance of the bridge, the resulting 'scale noise' will also be small.

Nevertheless, great care must be taken in the design of, and the

* Except if the torque meter is used, for instance, for the calibration of torque wrenches.

choice of materials for, slip-ring assemblies. Fig. 5.3*a* shows a fairly conventional arrangement with silver-carbon brushes on silver or stainless steel rings. In order to secure continuity of contact two or three brushes in parallel are spaced around the circumference of each ring. The brushes can usually be lifted off the rings when not in use.

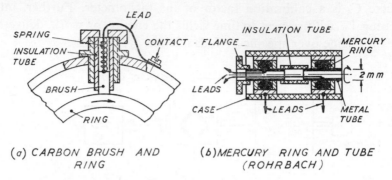

(*a*) CARBON BRUSH AND RING   (*b*)MERCURY RING AND TUBE (ROHRBACH)

Fig. 5.3 Slip-ring arrangements

At very high shaft speeds the slip-ring unit can no longer be built into the torque meter because the required large ring diameter would lead to excessively high circumferential velocities and thus to high brush wear and noise generation. In this case a separate slip-ring unit with ring diameters of 1 cm or less can be mounted externally to the torque meter. In the example shown in Fig. 5.4 the use of small-

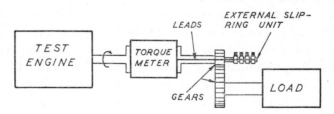

Fig. 5.4 External slip-ring unit mounted on gears

diameter external slip-rings has been made possible by the introduction of gears. In the experimental unit schematically shown in Fig. 5.3*b* the relative velocity has been reduced to a minimum; the ring has been replaced by a metal tube of only 2 mm diameter, rotating in a drop of mercury which forms a toroid around the tube. Since the contact resistance between the mercury ring and the rotating tube is low and continuous, the signal-to-noise ratio is good but, unfortunately, multiple slip-ring units of this kind tend to be rather long and difficult to align. There are also material problems raised by the peculiar properties of mercury.

If the strain gauges are operated in an a.c.-fed carrier system the slip-rings and brushes can be replaced by rotating and stationary transformer windings, respectively, which are designed to feed the rotating bridge circuit and also to extract the bridge output. These units are quite satisfactory if sufficient care has been taken in their design and manufacture to avoid axial movement between their windings or ferromagnetic cores which would generate spurious signals (noise) in the measuring circuit. Some advantage can be obtained from splitting each stationary winding in two halves, so that small air gap variations cancel out.

5.1.3   *Sting Balances*

In previous sections of this chapter we have been concerned with the measurement of unidirectional forces and couples. In this section we shall discuss an application of bonded strain gauges to the simultaneous measurement of three orthogonal forces and three similar moments in accordance with the six degrees of freedom associated with a solid body suspended in space. This problem occurs, for instance, in the investigation of the aerodynamic behaviour of aircraft models in wind-tunnels. The measuring apparatus is known as a *sting balance*, since at one end it is attached to a sting-type support; on the other it carries the model. The aerodynamic forces and moments exerted on the model are measured by strain gauges attached to the balance at suitable locations.

The insert to Fig. 5.5*a* shows the directions of normal, side and axial forces, and of yaw, pitch and roll moments experienced by the model in an air stream. A simplified view of a so-called *two-cage* sting balance machined from a solid block of high-tensile stainless steel is shown in the same figure. The positions of the (visible) strain gauges are indicated and their numbering agrees with that in the explanatory figures (*b*)–(*g*) below. The two identical cages on either end of the balance are used for the measurement of five components, i.e. normal (N) and side (S) forces, and yaw (Y), pitch (P) and roll

(R) moments. The axial (A) force is measured by the pick-off in the centre of the balance.

The normal force N represents lift and is usually the largest of the three forces; it therefore requires a fairly stiff bending structure. This is provided by the two vertical webs in the centre of the cages. Normal force N is derived from the bending mode of the balance in contre flexure, as shown in the side view of Fig. 5.5b. This figure also indicates the position of the four gauges near the top and bottom of the two webs and the type of strain (tensile ($+$), compressive ($-$)) induced by the normal force. The bridge circuit in the figure shows the gauge connections for maximum bridge output.

The pitch moment P (Fig. 5.5c) is measured by four gauges in similar locations on the webs, though the reader should notice that their positions (front and back of the webs) alternate for symmetry of strain distribution. However, the appropriate gauge connections in the bridge circuit differ from those of Fig. 5.5b.

Similar conditions apply to the measurement of side force S (Fig. 5.5d) and yaw moment Y (Fig. 5.5e), except that the gauges are now attached to four thin strips bridging the cage slots. (Only the two strips at the front of the balance are visible in Fig. 5.5a.)

The measurement of the axial force A, which is largely representative of drag, is probably the most difficult task. It is normally—and hopefully—assumed small, but the accuracy required in its measurement is particularly high in order to obtain a precise picture of the difference in aerodynamic performance of only slightly differing model shapes. Fig. 5.5a shows a simple axial flexure system of two solid bars at the top and bottom of the balance connected by two flat springs. Drag forces try to push the top bar to the right, thus exerting tensile strain in the thin (pre-tensioned) strip at the centre of the balance. A compressive strain of similar magnitude is produced by an inverted arrangement at the back of the balance (not visible). Although this simple scheme would produce push–pull strains which could be employed as shown in Fig. 5.5f, it would load the balance non-symmetrically. Improved methods of axial force measurement will be discussed presently.

Finally, the roll moment R is measured by two pairs of torque-sensing gauges attached to the top and bottom of the outer web surfaces of the cage nearer to the sting, as shown in Figs. 5.5a and g.

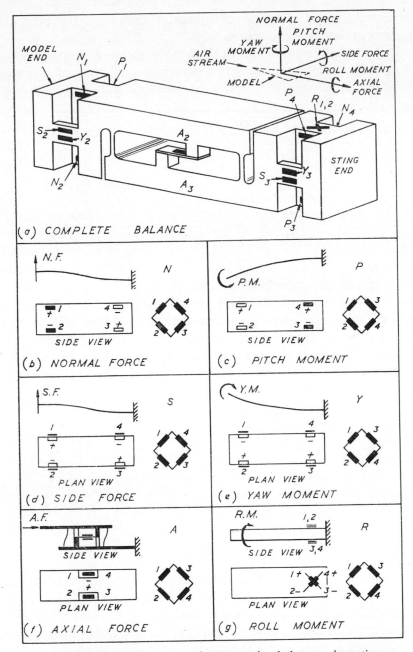

Fig. 5.5 Six-component strain gauge sting balance, schematic
(*Crown Copyright*)

The measurement of torque by means of 45° gauges has been explained in the previous section.

Perhaps the most difficult problem in the design and operation of sting balances is the control of interactions, in terms of spurious strains, between the six degrees of freedom. This is particularly

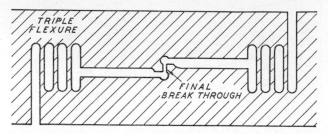

Fig. 5.6 Vertical cross-section through axis of sting balance
(*Crown Copyright*)

obvious with the large lift forces, which affect the measurement of low-level drag forces by bending distortions induced into the centre part of the balance. Our rather innocent design of Fig. 5.5 would be highly unsatisfactory from this aspect; a shape closer to reality is shown in Fig. 5.6 which would offer much greater resistance to bending forces. In this cross-sectional view of the axial plane the top

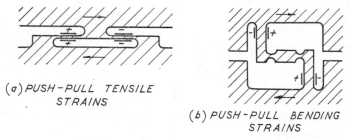

Fig. 5.7 Alternative methods of drag measurement
(*Crown Copyright*)

and bottom beams have been left as strong as possible, while the kinematics of the axial system has been improved by the triple flexures. In order to avoid 'flabbiness' during machining the two halves are separated by a final cut only at the very end of the machining process, as indicated in the figure.

The general problem of force interaction in strain gauge balances is rather complex. It requires a detail study of the three-dimensional pattern of distortions of active and passive members of the balance, and cannot be discussed here any further.

Two alternative methods for the measurements of axial forces are shown in Fig. 5.7. In (a), push–pull action and force symmetry with respect to both sides of the balance are obtained by two pairs of thin strips machined from the solid. Each side carries two tensile and two compressive gauges which are connected in series, thus providing the necessary four active bridge arms. Further improvement with respect to sensitivity can be achieved with the bending scheme of Fig. 5.7b. The machining of this double-cantilever arrangement is perhaps more elaborate, but also less critical, than that shown in (a).

5.1.4 *Principles of Gauge Selection*

The reader who has worked his way through Chapters 2 and 3 of this book probably needs little further advice on the selection of strain gauges for use in transducers. It will, therefore, suffice to summarise the major points pertaining to high-class strain gauge application.

(A) *Wire and Foil Gauges*

(a) Design your stressed transducer components for moderate strain levels, say $1{\cdot}0$–$1{\cdot}5 \times 10^{-3}$ m/m. At higher strains gauge hysteresis may have to be compensated for by opposing effects in strained transducer components.

(b) Select the longest gauge possible.

(c) Select the highest resistance possible. If the gauge output is to operate an indicator (e.g. galvanometer) without amplification, match the bridge resistance for maximum power transfer and optimum galvanometer damping.

(d) Select the most reliable gauge backing and bonding technique suitable for the specified temperature range. Follow the prescribed mounting procedure.

(e) Select gauge pairs matched for similarity of resistance and of thermal resistance variation.

(f) Mount your gauges on hardened surfaces; do not damage the surface after hardening by machining or sand blasting.

(*g*) Check gauges and gauge circuits for badly soldered joints.

(*h*) Compensate for thermal zero drift and gauge factor variation.

(*i*) Protect your gauge assembly by effective overcoating.

(*j*) Use reliable calibration methods for your transducers and provide for over-all calibration checks during measurement.

The most common high-stability strain gauge for use in precision transducers is still the flat-grid Constantan wire gauge on a phenolic or epoxy backing and mounted with due care by phenolic or epoxy cements. This arrangement will be suitable for accurate static and dynamic measurements at temperatures below 150°–200°C (see Fig. 2.4). It covers a wide range of precision strain gauge transducers, including load cells and sting balances. In the latter case, however, short gauge lengths are usually a regrettable necessity.

(*B*) *Semiconductor Gauges.* There are several transducers now on the market which employ semiconductor strain gauges as sensing elements. With their much higher gauge factor, it will be appreciated that for similar loads the stressed transducer components can be made much stiffer without loss in output. This desirable feature should appeal particularly to the designer of strain gauge balances, since increased stiffness reduces interaction. However, as has been shown in Chapter 3 on semiconductor strain gauge performance, they require extensive compensating effort in order to improve their inherent non-linearities and temperature sensitivities—a distinct disadvantage, which must be balanced carefully against their higher sensitivity. The advent of highly doped gauges of better linearity and improved temperature stability might, however, tip the scales in their favour in the near future.

A very recent development is flirting with the idea of producing semiconductor strain gauges as integral parts of a flexure system, by fusing the required kinds and amounts of impurities into selected areas of monolithic silicon crystals operating as force sensitive cantilevers or pressure sensitive diaphragms. This concept sounds quite attractive since small strain sensitive areas could thus be produced just where they are required without care for bonding problems. However, the mechanical strength of chunks of silicon is low and clamping is often unsatisfactory. (The great strength of thin silicon filaments and whiskers is a different matter.) Electrical insulation between adjacent conductive areas and lead attachment have also proved difficult. Much further development effort will be necessary to make this basically attractive technique suitable for practical use.

5.1.5   *Elements of Unbonded Strain Gauge Transducers*

Unbonded strain gauge transducers are basically extensometers, but since a well defined force is required to strain the suspended wire configuration they are also dynamometers. It is therefore convenient to discuss their peculiarities in the present context; their main application is, however, in the measurement of forces derived from pressure and acceleration (see sections 5.2 and 5.3 to follow).

An early version of a full-bridge unbonded strain sensing element is shown in Fig. 5.8. Two to twelve loops of high-tensile resistance

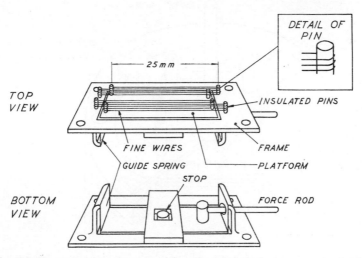

Fig. 5.8 Force-sensing element with unbonded strain gauges actuated by longitudinal movement of platform, schematic (Statham, Inc.)

wire (e.g. Alloy 479, Table 2.1) of about 0·001 in (0·025 mm) diameter are wound between insulated pins attached to both a stationary frame and a movable platform, so that at any longitudinal displacement of the platform relative to the frame two windings experience an increase and the other two a decrease in the initial wire tension produced by the winding process. Frame and platform are

F

made of aluminium alloy and the pins are either anodised aluminium or sapphire rods. The wire ends are taken to terminals (not shown in the figure) let into the frame.

The number of loops determine the reaction force of the dynamo-meter, and thus its range, except for the additional stiffness of the two flat guide springs which, however, are usually designed to be weak compared with the wire system. In order to avoid overloading the wires a stop is set to about $\pm 0.15\%$ maximum strain) Measuring forces are transmitted to the platform by means of a force rod.

The winding process of the gauge shown in Fig. 5.8 is made diffi-cult by the presence of adjacent pins. It requires great care and precision.

A more recent unbonded strain gauge element is shown in Fig. 5.9. The force rod acts on a cross-shaped double-beam system in contre

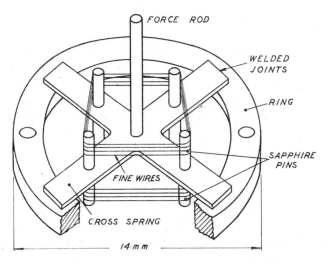

Fig. 5.9 Force-sensing element with unbonded strain gauges actuated by cross spring in contre flexure, schematic (Bell & Howell, Ltd./C.E.C.)

flexure which is welded to a solid ring. The sapphire pins are located at the points of inflexion, i.e. at maximum angular displacement of the beams. Each side of the cross carries two separate loops of high-tensile resistance wire of about 0·001 mm diameter which make up a complete Wheatstone bridge of about 350 ohms resistance. Because of the convenient positioning of the pins the winding process of this gauge is much simpler. Although the stiffness of the gauge wires is here no longer large in comparison with the bending stiffness of the cross spring, the reaction force of the element is still small compared with that of, for instance, a pressure sensing diaphragm. The main attraction of the design seems to lie in its radial symmetry which assists in the cancellation of spurious signals from transverse forces. Since the distances between the pins are short the effects of wire vibration are also reduced.

Besides the two typical sensing elements of Figs. 5.8 and 5.9 there are other arrangements of unbonded strain wires and flexural elements in common use, all serving much the same purpose and displaying similar characteristics. In general, the advantages and disadvantages of unbonded wire strain gauge transducers can be summarised thus:

(*A*) *Advantages.*

(*a*) Definite anchorage of the gauge wires at insulated pins guarantees low hysteresis and/or creep, since the danger of slip in backing and cement layers of bonded gauges is avoided.

(*b*) Faulty gauge installation by imperfect bonding caused by lack of skill and/or experience of the operator is eliminated.

(*c*) Miniaturisation of transducers is facilitated by integration of the force summing and force sensing components. Rugged transducer design is therefore feasible, in spite of the delicate strain wires, if the free lengths of the wires are kept short.

(*d*) Suitable for high-temperature environments, since the construction of unbonded gauges does not require the use of organic materials; soft-soldering can be replaced by welding.

(*B*) *Disadvantages.*

(*a*) Danger of slack wires dictates operation at low current densities. This is aggravated by bad heat dissipation from the freely suspended, in contrast to bonded, strain wires. Heatsinks positioned near the wires are not as effective as one would wish.

(*b*) Low overload ratios because of danger of wire breakage and/or slackness. Stops are usually incorporated.

(*c*) Higher cost.

A development which tends to overcome some of the disadvantages is the so-called *zero-length* unbonded gauge, which can best be understood by reference to Fig. 5.10. If, in (*a*), the point *B* is initially at the same vertical level as *A* (hence the name) both wires *AC* and *BC* carry half the weight of *W*. Now, if point *B* is lifted slowly, the load in *AC* is gradually transferred to *BC*, with the strains in the two wires varying in a push–pull fashion. The total range is determined by the highest possible strain exerted by *W* in *BC*, at which instant the wire *AC* would become slack.

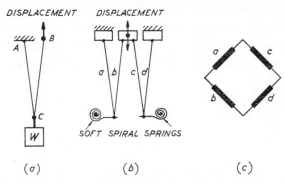

(*a*)   (*b*)   (*c*)

Fig. 5.10 'Zero-length' unbonded strain gauge (Statham, Inc.)

(*a*) Principle
(*b*) Full-bridge gauge
(*c*) Bridge circuit

In practical use the inconvenient weight is replaced by a soft, long spring which produces a constant strain bias virtually independent of displacement. Therefore, over-travel hardly increases the strain and consequently the wire can safely be operated very close to its elastic limit. Further, since heat generation cannot cause the wire to go slack, the gauge may also be operated at higher bridge input voltages than conventional unbonded gauges. Both properties combine in producing workable sensitivities said to be as high as 25 mV output per volt bridge input.

Fig. 5.10*b* illustrates the measurement of small forces derived, for instance, from a pressure sensitive diaphragm, by means of a four-wire arrangement. The bias strains are here produced by two soft spiral springs. The individual wires *a*, *b*, *c* and *d* are connected in bridge fashion, as shown in Fig. 5.10*c*. Transducers operating on this principle are offered commercially by the originators of the scheme. They are obviously less robust and compact than those based on a sensing element similar to the one shown in Fig. 5.9.

Mention should also be made of an application of what might loosely be called an unbonded semiconductor strain gauge. It consists of a bending cantilever with a slit which is bridged by a semiconductor strain gauge. A typical sensing element (the Pixie transducer of Endevco Corp. Pasadena, Calif., shown schematically in Fig. 5.11) has a sensitivity of 1·4% resistance variation per gramme

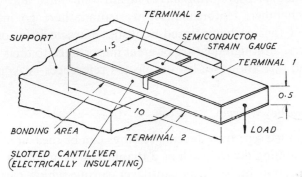

Fig. 5.11 Cantilever with unbonded semiconductor strain gauge, schematic (Endevco Corp.). Dimensions in mm

bending force at a gauge resistance of 400–750 ohms and a maximum gauge current of 15 mA. The highest permissible cantilever load is 40 gramme force. Contact with the gauge is made through gold-plated terminals 1 and 2 to which the gauge leads are attached. The inherent non-linearity and temperature dependence of the single semiconductor gauge of Fig. 5.11 can be improved by placing two units back-to-back for push–pull operation. Other arrangements of 'suspended' semiconductor gauges will occur to the reader (see also Fig. 5.22).

5.2 Pressure Transducers

Pressure measuring transducers constitute by far the largest contingent of all electrical transducers for industrial use, as well as for research and development work.

'Pressure' always means a pressure difference between two sides (i.e. inside and outside) of a pressure sensing device. Except for the rarer case of a small differential pressure superimposed on higher unknown base pressure, one of the two sides is usually at a well defined reference pressure, such as vacuum (*absolute pressure*), ambient pressure (*gauge pressure*) or any other given pressure level. *Differential pressure transducers*, therefore, have two working pressure inlets, *gauge pressure transducers* one inlet and a bleed to atmosphere, and *absolute pressure transducers* again one inlet and a built-in vacuum chamber. Unfortunately, we cannot here go into the intricacies of the mechanical and acoustic characteristics of pressure transducers, although they are of great importance to their successful design and operation (see list of selected references in Appendix C).

5.2.1   *Cantilever Types*

In strain gauge type transducers pressures can be measured by letting a force summing device, such as a diaphragm or a capsule, act on a flexible component, such as cantilever spring which carries strain gauges at locations of high strain. Fig. 5.12 shows examples of relevant arrangements in common use.

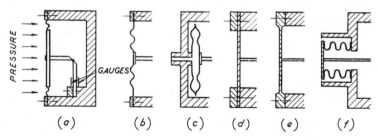

Fig. 5.12 Pressure sensing components for cantilever operation, schematic

(*a*) Piston-type diaphragm   (*d*) Flat clamped diaphragm
(*b*) Corrugated diaphragm   (*e*) Flat machined diaphragm
(*c*) Capsule   (*f*) Bellows

We shall ignore here the well known C-shaped Bourdon tube and its derivatives, the spiral or helical tubes and the 'twisted' tube, since they are rarely used with strain sensors, except perhaps for the occasional gauge plastered on in a hurry.

5.2.2   *Barrel Types*

Somewhat more sophisticated are the so-called *barrel gauges* of Fig.
5.13. The round barrel in (*a*) has usually two active sets of wires
wound around the hollow part and two dummy sets around the solid
part of the cylindrical element. On application of pressure to the

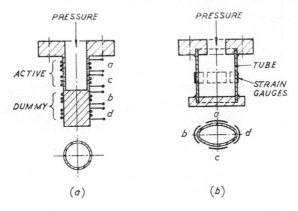

Fig. 5.13 Barrel-type pressure transducer, schematic

(*a*) Round tube
(*b*) Elliptical tube (Dean)

inside the tube expands in the shape of a barrel and there is an increase in resistance of windings *a* and *c*, while windings *b* and *d*
provide temperature compensation. For a thin-walled tube (i.e. wall
thickness small compared with tube radius) the tangential strain in
the wall at a pressure *p* (N/m²) is

$$e = \frac{pr}{Et}\left(1 - \frac{\nu}{2}\right) \quad \text{(m/m)} \tag{5.3}$$

where *r* (m) is the mean tube radius, *t* (m) the wall thickness, E (N/m²)
the Young's modulus and ν the Poisson's ratio of the tube material.

While the round barrel of Fig. 5.13*a* is suitable only for high
pressure ranges the elliptical tube in (*b*) covers lower ranges and has
a better overload ratio, since the tube walls deform into a circular
cross-section, prior to bursting. The bonded strain gauges *a* and *c*
are in tension, and *b* and *d* in compression. A Wheatstone bridge
with four active arms can thus be arranged.

5.2.3 *Diaphragm Types*

In this section we shall discuss transducers with strain gauges bonded to a pressure sensitive diaphragm. Unfortunately, this appears to be such an obvious scheme that one seldom questions the efficiency of this apparently simple and common-sense arrangement.

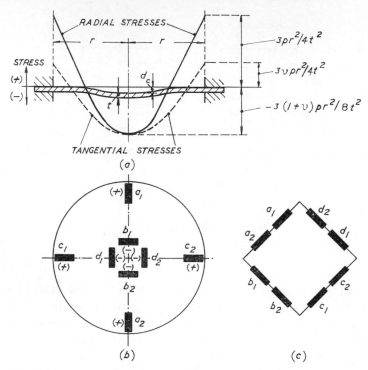

Fig. 5.14 Strain gauging of a pressurised thin flat diaphragm, schematic
(*a*) Radial and tangential stresses
(*b*) Gauge arrangement on diaphragm
(*c*) Gauges in bridge circuit

The stress distribution at small deflections, or loads, of a thin flat diaphragm securely clamped at its circumference is shown in Fig. 5.14*a*, where the symbols in the formulae have the usual meaning. It is seen—and commonly realised—that a complete bridge can be formed by at least two tensile gauges positioned in a radial direction near the circumference, and two compressive gauges in tangential directions near the centre of the diaphragm, thus taking advantage of maximum push–pull strain at these locations. Fig. 5.14b shows a symmetrical arrangement with a total of eight gauges, and Fig. 5.14c the corresponding bridge circuit.

In fact, printed strain gauges exist which are designed to cover the whole area of a given diaphragm by a foil pattern with (radial) meanders around the circumference and (tangential) spirals about the centre, but the real trouble is the low level of strain in a well behaved diaphragm which requires (a) the strain/pressure relationship to be linear, and (b) the diaphragm stresses to be kept within safe limits.

(A) *Condition of Linearity.* It can be shown that the condition of linearity of strain in a thin diaphragm clamped at its circumference and loaded uniformly by a pressure p (N/m²) is satisfied by the useful rule-of-thumb that its centre deflection must not exceed half the diaphragm thickness, i.e.:

$$d_c = \frac{3(1 - v^2)r^4 p}{16Et^3} \leqslant t/2 \quad \text{(m)}. \tag{5.4}$$

The maximum pressure for linear strain operation is therefore

$$p_{max} \leqslant \frac{8E}{3(1 - v^2)}\left(\frac{t}{r}\right)^4 \quad \text{(N/m²)}. \tag{5.5}$$

Equation 5.5 has been plotted in Fig. 5.15a for both steel and dural diaphragms (see Table 4.2 for values of E and v). Note that at a realistic aspect ratio of $r/t \approx 100$ the useful linear pressure range is only about 1 lb/in². Much higher ranges are not permissible because of excessive diaphragm stresses, as will be shown presently.

(B) *Condition of Safe Stresses.* Besides the condition (A) of linearity the diaphragm must not be operated beyond a safe value of stress pertaining to the particular material and mode of loading. Remembering that transducer diaphragms are bent to and fro many times in the course of their duties, safe bending stresses for typical steel diaphragms are around 75×10^6 N/m² (11,000 lb/in²) and for dural diaphragms 30×10^6 N/m².

We now compute the maximum radial stress at the circumference at various values of aspect ratio r/t from the equation

$$\sigma = \tfrac{3}{4}p_{max}\left(\frac{r}{t}\right)^2 \quad \text{(N/m²)} \tag{5.6}$$

*

with p_{max} obtained from equation 5.5, in order to secure linear calibration. Then we cut off at the safe stresses quoted above (Fig. 5.15*b*). The corresponding strain curves ($e = \sigma/E$) are plotted in Fig. 5.15*c*.

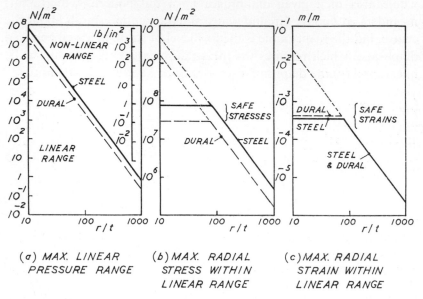

(*a*) MAX. LINEAR
PRESSURE RANGE

(*b*) MAX. RADIAL
STRESS WITHIN
LINEAR RANGE

(*c*) MAX. RADIAL
STRAIN WITHIN
LINEAR RANGE

Fig. 5.15 Maximum pressures, stresses and strains of flat circular steel and duralumin diaphragms with linear calibration at safe stresses, as functions of diaphragm aspect ratio r/t

Although for thick diaphragms ($r/t \rightarrow 10$) our simple approach is strictly not valid, this range is obviously not very attractive, anyway, since maximum strain is here constant and the sensitivity (strain versus pressure), therefore, declines towards greater diaphragm thicknesses. At high aspect ratios ($r/t \rightarrow 1000$) the useful linear pressure range falls off rapidly (Fig. 5.15*a*) and the measurable strain vanishes (Fig. 5.15*c*).

The most useful diaphragms have aspect ratios around 100, but even in this area the maximum radial strain at the circumference is well below 0·1%. Since practical strain gauges must be located at some distance away from the clamping region the actually available strain is smaller still (see Fig. 5.14).

Some improvement in strain level may be achieved by employing better materials with higher Young's moduli and safe stresses. However, the gain is not spectacular and the danger of fatigue fracture and of increased hysteresis sets distinct limits to substantially higher working stresses.

Therefore, in spite of the apparent simplicity of the scheme, the use of bonded strain gauges on flat pressure sensitive diaphragms is severely restricted by the low strain levels attainable under conditions of linear calibration and reasonable diaphragm stresses. For wire and foil gauges—whether single gauges or elaborate etched-foil patterns—the lack of useful strain means low gauge output which might result in an insufficient signal-to-noise ratio. Evaporated *thin-film* strain gauges and, of course, *semiconductor* gauges have been suggested as remedies; they might be able to put some new life into this rather frustrated scheme.

5.2.4   *Unbonded Types*

Unbonded strain gauge pressure transducers consist of a pressure sensing component, such as those shown in Fig. 5.12, and a force sensing element with suspended wire arrangements, as discussed in section 5.1.5 and shown in Figs. 5.8–5.10. Other wire arrangements are also known; in particular Fig. 5.16 shows a type which partly resembles the barrel gauge of Fig. 5.13*a* and partly the sensing element of Fig. 5.9 with tilting pins. Here a flange attached to a thin-walled tube deforms under internal pressure in the shape

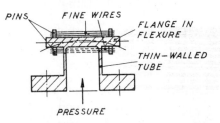

Fig. 5.16 'Mushroom'-type unbonded strain gauge pressure transducer, schematic

of a mushroom, or umbrella, and push–pull strain variation occurs in the wire loops wound over the pins above and below the flange.

Unbonded strain gauge pressure transducers on the market are usually high-class instruments with accuracies of calibration of $\pm 0.5\%$ of full scale, or better. Particular care is taken in the design and manufacture of the diaphragm unit, which is often precision welded to its supports and thus combines the virtues of an integrated diaphragm with greater ease and precision in manufacture.

Absolute pressure gauges with built-in vacuum chambers have posed severe problems of leakage, particularly if a long shelf life is expected, but, on the whole, they are now quite satisfactory. Reliable pressure seals have also been developed for the higher pressure ranges and for gauges with high base pressures, and the problem of compatibility of materials, for instance in the presence of a corrosive pressure medium, is usually not insurmountable.

The suppression of spurious signals from acceleration and vibration is closely connected with the dynamic response of pressure transducers, and cannot be discussed here, except for the rather obvious advice—applicable to all types of pressure transducers—to design their moving parts as light as possible, so that for a given strain producing compliance the mechanical input impedance is as high as possible. The effects of secondary resonances of, for instance, suspended lengths of gauge wire, must be controlled carefully.

5.3   Acceleration Transducers

According to Newton's second law of dynamics,

$$F = aM. \tag{5.7}$$

This permits the measurement, in terms of force F (N), of acceleration a (m/s^2) acting on a mass M (kg).* In engineering it is, however, more important to know by what factor n the (dynamic) load on a structure is increased by the effect of acceleration, as compared with the gravitational load

$$F_g = gM \tag{5.8}$$

where $g \approx 9{\cdot}81$ m/s^2 is the acceleration due to gravity. The range of an accelerometer, then, is quoted in multiples of g:

$$F = nF_g = ngM. \tag{5.9}$$

* The newton (N), actually, is defined as the force that is required to accelerate a mass of 1 kg by 1 meter per second per second (see Appendix A).

Acceleration transducers, therefore, consist essentially of a seismic mass supported by a compliant element which serves as a force indicator. In the present context its deformation under acceleration is measured by means of strain gauges. Fig. 5.17 shows two elementary strain gauge acceleration transducers. In (*a*) the gauges are

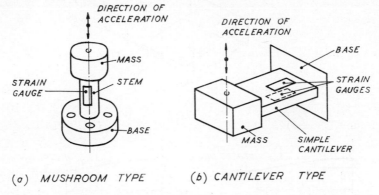

(a) MUSHROOM TYPE   *(b)* CANTILEVER TYPE

Fig. 5.17 Elementary linear-acceleration transducers with bonded strain gauges

bonded to a centre stem which carries the seismic mass. In practice, this design is useful for the measurement of only very high accelerations which are capable of generating measurable strains in a reasonably proportioned transducer of this kind. Also, because of spurious bending stresses, the strain distribution over the stem surface would normally not be uniform.

At ordinary acceleration levels the simple cantilever beam of Fig. 5.17*b* is a more efficient strain generator, and this basic form—or derivations of it—is used in many strain-gauge type accelerometers. It is, therefore, opportune to take a closer look at its performance, particularly with respect to acceleration applied also in directions normal to the main direction (*transverse sensitivity*).

5.3.1   *Cantilever Types*

The strain in a simple cantilever with strain gauges of finite lengths attached near its clamping point is given in Fig. 5.1*c*. For the accelerometer the load *F* is obtained from equations 5.7 or 5.9, if (*a*) the direction of acceleration is strictly normal to the cantilever axis, and

(b) the deflection at the tip of the beam is small. However, in many practical applications conditions (a) and (b) are not satisfied. Since the bending stiffness of the cantilever beam to forces acting in the y-direction (see Fig. 5.18a) is usually very high, we shall ignore their

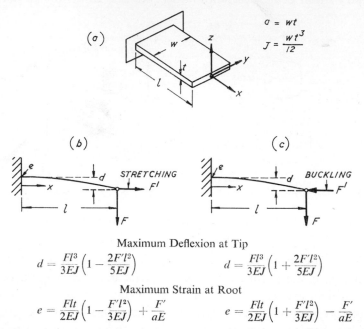

Maximum Deflexion at Tip

$$d = \frac{Fl^3}{3EJ}\left(1 - \frac{2F'l^2}{5EJ}\right) \qquad\qquad d = \frac{Fl^3}{3EJ}\left(1 + \frac{2F'l^2}{5EJ}\right)$$

Maximum Strain at Root

$$e = \frac{Flt}{2EJ}\left(1 - \frac{F'l^2}{3EJ}\right) + \frac{F'}{aE} \qquad e = \frac{Flt}{2EJ}\left(1 + \frac{F'l^2}{3EJ}\right) - \frac{F'}{aE}$$

Fig. 5.18 Tip deflection and root strain of simple cantilever with transverse and longitudinal bending forces

effect here, but a particularly interesting situation arises if acceleration forces occur simultaneously in the x- and z-directions. Figs. 5.18b and c show schematic side views of a deflected cantilever with the main acceleration force F pointing downwards in both cases, while a longitudinal acceleration force F' produces additional tension or compression along the cantilever axis. For any values of F and F' the expressions for tip deflection and root strain are complex (with slightly different laws applicable to tension and compression), but if F' is not excessive as compared with F, then the approximate formulae given in Fig. 5.18 hold.

It is seen that a tensile force F' decreases the normal tip deflection produced by F alone, while compression increases it. The same is true for the contribution of F' to bending strain, where the last term, F'/aE, in the strain equation is, of course, either positive or negative, depending on the direction of F'. Since the effect of F' on displacement as well as on strain varies with l^2/EJ, this kind of transverse sensitivity can be reduced by making the cantilever as short and as stiff as possible, as would be expected.

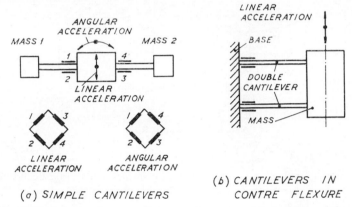

Fig. 5.19 Acceleration transducers, schematic, with double cantilevers

Fig. 5.19a shows a double cantilever arrangement which, in principle, can be used to measure both linear and angular acceleration, depending on how the four strain gauges are connected in a Wheatstone bridge circuit. A practical difficulty with this arrangement may, however, arise in dynamic measurements, since the natural frequencies of the two cantilever systems are bound to differ slightly and a low-frequency beat signal will appear in the recorded output, unless the transducer is well damped. Unfortunately, we cannot go here any further into the fascinating problem of the dynamic performance of acceleration transducers; books dealing more fully with the mechanical aspects of transducer performance and design are listed in Appendix C.

The basic idea of an acceleration transducer with two parallel springs operating in contre flexure is shown in Fig. 5.19b. This very popular arrangement avoids the tilting movement of the seismic mass attached to a simple cantilever and thus generally facilitates the design of the transducer, particularly with respect to the proper dimensioning of gaps and channels for the damping fluid.

The effect of longitudinal forces on the contre-flexural beam is reduced appreciably, as can be seen from Fig. 5.20 when compared with Fig. 5.18 for the simple cantilever. This still applies under conditions of equal tip deflections, i.e. to acceleration transducers of similar natural frequencies.

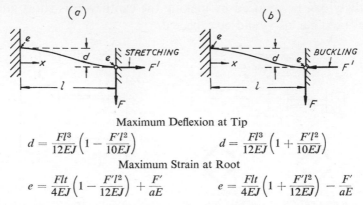

Maximum Deflexion at Tip

$$d = \frac{Fl^3}{12EJ}\left(1 - \frac{F'l^2}{10EJ}\right) \qquad\qquad d = \frac{Fl^3}{12EJ}\left(1 + \frac{F'l^2}{10EJ}\right)$$

Maximum Strain at Root

$$e = \frac{Flt}{4EJ}\left(1 - \frac{F'l^2}{12EJ}\right) + \frac{F'}{aE} \qquad\qquad e = \frac{Flt}{4EJ}\left(1 + \frac{F'l^2}{12EJ}\right) - \frac{F'}{aE}$$

Fig. 5.20 Tip deflection and root strain of cantilever in contre flexure with transverse and longitudinal bending forces

5.3.2 *Unbonded Types*

Acceleration type transducers have also been designed around the unbonded force sensing elements described in section 5.1.5. Fig. 5.21 shows two typical examples. In (*a*) the seismic mass is supported by

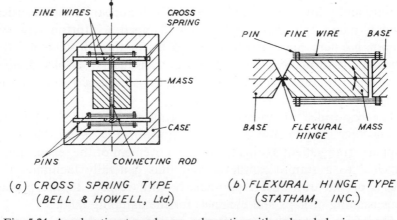

(*a*) CROSS SPRING TYPE   (*b*) FLEXURAL HINGE TYPE
     (BELL & HOWELL, Ltd.)   (STATHAM, INC.)

Fig. 5.21 Acceleration transducers, schematic, with unbonded wire sensors

two elements shown in greater detail in Fig. 5.9. By virtue of the springs being in contre flexure (see previous section) and since the design is almost perfectly symmetrical about its axis, the transverse sensitivity is expected to be low.

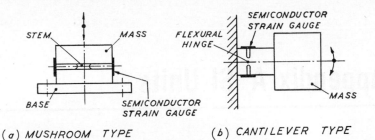

(*a*) *MUSHROOM TYPE*   (*b*) *CANTILEVER TYPE*

Fig. 5.22 Acceleration transducers, schematic, with unbonded semiconductor strain gauges (Duffield)

The arrangement of Fig. 5.21*b* is particularly suitable for low acceleration ranges; otherwise its characteristics are somewhat similar to those of a simple cantilever.

Finally, the principle of the 'unbonded semiconductor strain gauge' of Fig. 5.11 can also be applied to acceleration transducers. Fig. 5.22 shows two suggested arrangements schematically. Temperature effects could be compensated by positioning inactive gauges of the same kind near the active gauges.

Appendix A SI Units

The inconvenience of having to struggle with several systems of units is a common and painful experience of the practising scientist and engineer. Through the years he had a choice of two 'absolute' CGS systems (with electromagnetic and electrostatic units), and several 'practical' systems with various English or metric units, or with mixtures of all. The physicist is familiar enough with the odd factors of 3, 9, 2π, 4π and powers of 10, which continuously occur in the CGS system. The engineer on the Continent has his fair share of these in his metric engineering units, while the English and American engineering units have produced their own crop of unlikely conversion factors.

In fact, the basic mechanical units of length, mass and time are fairly easily decided upon; it is the inclusion of the electromagnetic units that have caused all the trouble. However, in 1904 G. Giorgi showed that, if the unit of length be the metre, the unit mass the kilogramme, the unit time the second and the permeability of empty space $\mu_0 = 4\pi \times 10^{-7}$, then the electromagnetic and the electrostatic systems would both be satisfied by these practical units, and the factors 2π and 4π would now become meaningful insofar, as they would occur in systems with cylindrical and spherical symmetry, respectively. The purist might, however, object that in the MKS system the dimensional identities between the magnetic quantities B and H, and between the electrical quantities D and E are lost, since μ_0 and ε_0 ($= 1/(36\pi \times 10^9) = 8 \cdot 859 \times 10^{-12}$) are no longer unity.

Serious discussions of Giorgi's system did not start before 1935, but in 1948 the Ninth International Conference on Weights and Measures adopted an MKS system with μ_0 as the fourth basic unit. Then, in 1950, the I.E.C. adopted the ampere (defined by Ampère's law as the steady current in two infinite, straight and parallel conductors of negligible cross-section, one metre apart, which produce in vacuum a force equal to 2×10^{-7} newton per metre length), creating the MKSA (or Giorgi) system. The Tenth CGPM in 1954 adopted a rationalised and coherent system of units based on the four MKSA units, the degree Kelvin and the candela. The Eleventh CGPM in 1960 formally gave it the full title 'Système International d'Unités', for which the abbreviation is SI in all languages. A list of basic, supplementary and derived units of this system is given below.

Quantity	Unit	Symbol of unit
1. Basic units		
1. length	metre	m
2. mass	kilogramme	kg
3. time	second	s
4. intensity of electric current	ampere	A
5. thermodynamic temperature	degree Kelvin	°K
6. luminous intensity	candela	cd
2. Supplementary units		
7. plane angle	radian	rad
8. solid angle	steradian	sr
3. Derived units		
9. area	square metre	m^2
10. volume	cubic metre	m^3
11. frequency	hertz; or cycles per second	Hz; c/s
12. density	kilogramme per cubic metre	kg/m^3
13. speed	metre per second	m/s
14. angular velocity	radian per second	rad/s
15. acceleration	metre per second squared	m/s^2
16. angular acceleration	radian per second squared	rad/s^2
17. force	newton	N; $kg\ m/s^2$
18. pressure; stress	newton per square metre	N/m^2
19. viscosity, dynamic	newton-second per square metre	$N\ s/m^2$
20. viscosity, kinematic	square metre per second	m^2/s
21. work; energy; quantity of heat	joule	J; N m; Ws
22. power	watt	W; J/s
23. quantity of electricity	coulomb	C; A s
24. electric tension; potential difference; electromotive force	volt	V; W/A
25. electric field strength	volt per metre	V/m
26. electric resistance	ohm	Ω; V/A
27. electric capacity	farad	F; A s/V
28. magnetic flux	weber	Wb
29. inductance	henry	H; V s/A
30. magnetic flux density	tesla	T; Wb/m^2
31. magnetic field strength	ampere (turn) per metre	A/m
32. magnetomotive force	ampere (turn)	A
33. luminous flux	lumen	lm; cd sr
34. luminance	candela per square metre	cd/m^2
35. illumination	lux	lx; lm/m^2

As a general rule for the 'spelling', symbols of units derived from proper names are represented by capitals, e.g. N, H, V, K, T, etc., and all plural 's', and full stops, are omitted. Note that m/m means metre (elongation) per metre (length), not millimetre (mm). The inverse of resistance (conductance) is written Ω^{-1}, or ohm^{-1}, not mho(s). (Also, 1 siemens $= 1 \ \Omega^{-1}$.)

The names and symbols of the multiples and submultiples are:

Factor	Prefix	Symbol
10^{12}	tera	T
10^9	giga	G
10^6	mega	M
10^3	kilo	k
10^2	hecto	h
10^1	deca	da
10^{-1}	deci	d
10^{-2}	centi	c
10^{-3}	milli	m
10^{-6}	micro	μ
10^{-9}	nano	n
10^{-12}	pico	p

Note the difference between M (mega) and m (milli); k (kilo) is a lower-case letter.

Appendix B Conversion Tables

The conversions listed in the following tables are those likely to occur in strain gauging and related subjects. They are restricted to the relationships of SI units to English and Continental engineering units; conversions to and from the CGS system have been omitted, except for magnetic units, where 'gauss' and 'maxwell' have also been used in engineering.

1. Length

		m	in	ft	yd
1 m	=	1	39·37	3·281	1·093
1 in	=	$2·54 \times 10^{-2}$	1	$8·333 \times 10^{-2}$	$2·778 \times 10^{-2}$
1 ft	=	0·3048	12	1	0·3333
1 yd	=	0·9144	36	3	1

1 thou (U.K.) = 1 mil (U.S.A.) = 10^{-3} in = $2·54 \times 10^{-5}$ m.

2. Area

		m^2	in^2	ft^2	yd^2
1 m^2	=	1	1550	10·76	1·196
1 in^2	=	$6·452 \times 10^{-4}$	1	$6·944 \times 10^{-3}$	$7·716 \times 10^{-4}$
1 ft^2	=	$9·29 \times 10^{-2}$	144	1	0·1111
1 yd^2	=	0·8361	1296	9	1

1 circular mil* = $7·854 \times 10^{-7}$ in^2 = $5·067 \times 10^{-10}$ m^2.

3. Volume

		m^3	in^3	ft^3	yd^3
1 m^3	=	1	$6·102 \times 10^4$	35·31	1·308
1 in^3	=	$1·639 \times 10^{-5}$	1	$5·787 \times 10^{-4}$	$2·144 \times 10^{-5}$
1 ft^3	=	$2·832 \times 10^{-2}$	1728	1	$3·704 \times 10^{-2}$
1 yd^3	=	0·7645	$4·666 \times 10^4$	27	1

1 U.K. gal = 1·201 U.S.A. gal = $4·546 \times 10^{-3}$ m^3.
1 l = 1·000028 dm^3.

* Circular area of 10^{-3} inch diameter.

153

4. Angle

		radian	degree	minute	second
1 radian	=	1	57·30	3438	$2·063 \times 10^{-5}$
1 degree	=	$1·745 \times 10^{-2}$	1	60	3600
1 minute	=	$2·909 \times 10^{-4}$	$1·667 \times 10^{-2}$	1	60
1 second	=	$4·848 \times 10^{-6}$	$2·778 \times 10^{-4}$	$1·667 \times 10^{-2}$	1

5. Mass

		kg	lb	slug	U.K. ton
1 kg	=	1	2·205	$6·852 \times 10^{-2}$	$9·842 \times 10^{-4}$
1 lb	=	0·4536	1	$3·108 \times 10^{-2}$	$4·464 \times 10^{-4}$
1 slug	=	14·59	32·17	1	$1·436 \times 10^{-2}$
1 U.K. ton	=	1016	2240	69·62	1

1 U.S.A. ton = 0·8929 U.K. ton = 907·2 kg.
1 tonne = 10^3 kg.

6. Force

		N	lbf*	pdl	kgf*
1 N	=	1	0·2248	7·233	0·1020
1 lbf*	=	4·448	1	32·17	0·4536
1 pdl	=	0·1383	$3·108 \times 10^{-2}$	1	$1·410 \times 10^{-2}$
1 kgf*	=	9·807	2·205	70·93	1

7. Stress, pressure

		N/m²	lbf/in²	U.K. ton/in²	kgf/cm²
1 N/m²	=	1	$1·450 \times 10^{-4}$	$6·473 \times 10^{-8}$	$1·020 \times 10^{-5}$
1 lbf/in²	=	$6·895 \times 10^3$	1	$4·464 \times 10^{-4}$	$7·031 \times 10^{-2}$
1 U.K. ton/in²	=	$1·544 \times 10^7$	2240	1	157·5
1 kgf/cm²	=	$9·807 \times 10^4$	14·22	$6·348 \times 10^{-3}$	1

1 standard atmosphere = 760 torr = 1013 mb = $1·013 \times 10^5$ N/m².

8. Power

		W	HP	ft lbf/s	m kgf/s
1 W	=	1	$1·341 \times 10^{-3}$	0·7376	0·1020
1 HP	=	745·7	1	550	76·04
1 ft lbf/s	=	1·356	$1·818 \times 10^{-3}$	1	0·1383
1 m kgf/s	=	9·807	$1·315 \times 10^{-2}$	7·233	1

1 BTU/hr = 0·2931 W.
1 PS = 75 m kgf/s = 0·986 HP = 735·5 W.

* 1 lbf = 1 lb force; 1 kgf = 1 kg force, etc. 1 kilopond = 1 kgf.

9. Energy, work, heat

		J	kWh	ft lbf	m kgf
1 J	=	1	$2 \cdot 778 \times 10^{-7}$	$0 \cdot 7376$	$0 \cdot 1020$
1 kWh	=	$3 \cdot 600 \times 10^6$	1	$2 \cdot 655 \times 10^6$	$3 \cdot 671 \times 10^5$
1 ft lbf	=	$1 \cdot 356$	$3 \cdot 766 \times 10^{-7}$	1	$0 \cdot 1383$
1 m kgf	=	$9 \cdot 807$	$2 \cdot 724 \times 10^{-6}$	$7 \cdot 233$	1

1 BTU $= 1 \cdot 055 \times 10^3$ J $= 2 \cdot 930 \times 10^{-4}$ kWh.
1 eV (electron volt) $= 1 \cdot 602 \times 10^{-19}$ J.

10. Magnetic units

Magnetomotive force: 1 ampere-turn $= 1 \cdot 257$ gilbert.
Magnetic field strength: 1 ampere-turn/m $= 1 \cdot 257 \times 10^{-2}$ oersted.
Magnetic flux: 1 weber $= 10^8$ maxwell.
Magnetic flux density: 1 tesla $= 1$ weber/m$^2 = 10^4$ gauss.

11. Resistivity

1 ohm m $= 6 \cdot 011 \times 10^8$ ohm-cir.mil/ft.

Appendix C Some Books for Further Reading

Chapter 1

(a) LEE, G. H. *An Introduction to Experimental Stress Analysis*. Wiley & Sons, New York (1950).
(b) HETÉNYI, M. (Ed.) *Handbook of Experimental Stress Analysis*. Wiley & Sons, New York (1950).
(c) DALLY, J. W. and RILEY, W. F. *Experimental Stress Analysis*. McGraw-Hill, New York (1965).
(d) ZIENKIEWICZ, O. C. and HOLISTER, G. S. *Stress Analysis; Recent Developments in Numerical and Experimental Methods*. Wiley & Sons, New York (1965).

Chapter 2

(a) DOBIE, W. B. and ISAAC, P. C. G. *Electrical Resistance Strain Gauges*. Engl. Univ. Press, London (1948).
(b) YARNELL, J. *Resistance Strain Gauges*. Electronic Engineering Monograph, London (1951).
(c) *Characteristics and Application of Resistance Strain Gages*. Nat. Bur. Stand. Circular Nr. 528 (1954).
(d) PERRY, C. C. and LISSNER, H. R. *The Strain Gage Primer*. McGraw-Hill, New York (1955; 2nd ed. 1962).
(e) MURRAY, W. M. and STEIN, P. K. *Strain Gage Techniques*. MIT Press, Cambridge, Mass. (1956).
(f) *Baldwin–Lima–Hamilton Strain Gage Handbook*.
(g) *Philips Guide to Strain Gauges*.

Chapter 3

(a) DEAN, M. III and DOUGLAS, R. D. *Semiconductor and Conventional Strain Gages*. Acad. Press, New York (1962).
(b) *Baldwin–Lima–Hamilton Semiconductor Strain Gage Handbook*. Parts I–VI.

Chapter 4

(*a*) TIMOSHENKO, S. P. and GOODIER, J. N. *Theory of Elasticity*. McGraw-Hill, New York (1951).
(*b*) HOUWINK, R. *Elasticity, Plasticity and Structure of Matter*. Dover Publ., New York (1952).

Chapter 5

(*a*) LION, K. S. *Instrumentation in Scientific Research; Electrical Input Transducers*. McGraw-Hill, New York (1959).
(*b*) NEUBERT, H. K. P. *Instrument Transducers*. Clarendon Press, Oxford Univ. Press, Oxford (1963).

Index

To the Reader

The author and publisher would welcome suggestions towards future editions of this book, or the pointing out of any misprint or obscurity. Please write to the Technical Editor, Macmillan and Co. Ltd., Little Essex Street, W.C.2.